GAMES FOR INSOMNIACS

John G. Fuller

GAMES FOR INSOMNIACS

or: A Lifetime Supply of
   Insufferable Brain Twisters

ILLUSTRATED BY DOUG ANDERSON

Funk & Wagnalls
NEW YORK

list of events

Whether you live in Near, Miss., or Ballpoint, Penn., you'll have a chance here to demonstrate something or other about geography. If you're a sport, you'll try the Game Section at the end of the chapter first. If not, you're probably more sensible.

If you call somebody who is a registered slob *uncouth,* why not call his opposited counterpart *couth?* Or if someone is *ept,* why isn't he skilful and full of aptitude? If a president is kicked out of office, why isn't he *augurated?* Or if you don't read this chapter, you're *trepid.*

Suppose you went to a reception and met at this gathering Norman Rockwell, Rockwell Kent, Norman Kent, John Cecil Holmes, John Clellon Holmes, Tennessee Ernie Ford and Tennessee Williams, how would you react? Or how *wouldn't* you react? This decision is yours, after you read or try the games in this chapter.

Someday, you might be greeted by a member of the press who introduces himself to you by saying: "I'm Brown— from the *Sun.*" If this ever happens, you won't really be prepared for it until you spring some of the games in this chapter on your friends, or on your self for that matter.

If lawyers are disbarred and priests are unfrocked, why aren't electricians delighted and musicians denoted? This whole thing is very logical, and you'll enjoy both trying the game and reading the chapter if you don't ruin too many nights' sleep first.

Did you know there is a restaurant which has on its menu Young Whale Stuffed with New Buick ($3500) or Roast Suckling Pig, with bottle, nipple and Simulac ($2.25)? Or did you hear about the mystery writer who ordered Mints Spy and Scrambled Yeggs? Either way, this chapter is waiting for you to pit your wit against it.

Have you heard about the East Indian potentate who was overrun by elephants so that his reign was called on account of game? Here are all the switcheroos you can cope with, either in reading or game form, and the rest is up to you.

You'll never believe how many sentences you can find which have every letter in the alphabet in them, and which can replace the famous old test sentence THE QUICK BROWN FOX JUMPS OVER THE LAZY DOG. There's a whole story which goes with this which will grip you like a bottle of rubber cement.

PREAMBLE

A favorite story of mine is told by Gerald Lieberman, the writer and anthologist. It concerns a wife who despaired about pleasing her husband with her cooking. When her psychiatrist asked her what she fed him, she said:

"Well, I bought a twelve-pound rabbit. Monday I gave him rabbit steak. Tuesday, rabbit's feet. Wednesday, barbecued rabbit spare ribs. Thursday, rabbit hamburger. Friday, goulash à la rabbit."

"That's interesting," the analyst remarked. "What did he say on Friday?"

"Nothing," sobbed the wife. "He just sat there and stared at me with those big, pink eyes!"

I hadn't been writing the TRADE WINDS column in the *Saturday Review* very long, when I discovered that many people avoid both rabbits and psychiatrists in one particular way: They either invent games for themselves, or they flagellate themselves trying to figure out other people's brain twisters. Or they spring them on unsuspecting guests with a fiendish delight, sitting back and relishing their discomfort. From the amount of mail I get concerning this Machiavellian indoor sport, I'm convinced that it is a disease which has not been diagnosed, and perhaps never will be.

But perhaps this is all to the good. Life can be pretty dull without some minor irritations to liven it up. Too many of us go around looking gloomy half the time, like the woman whose cat was run over by the village steamroller. She didn't say anything. She just stood there with a long puss.

Most of the games and brain twisters in this book have proven to be contagious, but I hope pleasantly so. As long as this warning is stated, my conscience is clear. It's a little like the neophyte yachtsman who decided to decorate his boat with some bright signal flags, which he chose at random. As soon as they were hoisted, every boat in the harbor slipped anchor and left port. It was only later that he learned the meaning of the flags he had put up: SMALLPOX ABOARD. COMING TO YOUR ASSISTANCE. These same flags might well be posted here.

Comedian Ed Wynn has a story which he claims is absolutely sure fire, regardless of where or when it is told. Yet no one has ever been able to define just *why* it gets a laugh. In bare outline, the story tells of a couple asleep in bed in the middle of the night. A noise is heard downstairs. The wife wakes the husband.

"Go see what it's about!" she whispers.

The husband gets up, cold, tired, and sleepy. He throws a blanket over his shoulder and creeps downstairs. When he gets to the bottom of the stairs, a huge, clawed, furry arm reaches out of the darkness and snatches the blanket away. The husband rushes back upstairs, jumps into bed, and pulls the covers over his head.

"Did you find out what it's about?" asks the wife.

"Yes," says the trembling husband. "It's about the blanket!"

Well, this book is about games. And no one can tell why they have kept so many people busy either figuring them out, or adding more material to them.

Some of them are good for around the dinner table, after dinner, or even at breakfast if you're awake enough to talk. Others are sort of private games and twisters, the kind you try to mull over in bed in place of counting sheep or your weakening debentures. Others might require a sharp pencil, an inquiring mind, and a mug of strong coffee. Some are really not games at all, they're just things to think about. Some are old and hoary, as ridiculous as the customer who came into the antique shop and asked: "What's new?"

I'm indebted to hundreds of fellow insomniacs who have shared their tortured brain-wrigglings with me. They have proved themselves to be as obsessional as the geometry professor who muttered: "I love my wife, but oh, Euclid!"

Recently, some scientists have been reported working on an English-to-Russian translating machine. To test the device, they fed it the sentence: "The spirit is willing, but the flesh is weak." (This is not to be confused with the liquid-fuel rocket with bad ignition, which failed to go off because the spirits were willing, but the flash was weak.) Within seconds, the translating machine came back with: "The liquor is good, but the food is lousy." Sometimes an idea for a game is good, but it doesn't suit all people. This is understandable, and not to be deplored. I hope there is enough variety here so that you can skip those which aren't quite your dish of tea.

There's really no need to be sad and downcast if you can't do all these games. I've known some people who can't solve a game who act like actor-director Romney Brent's cat. It came home from the kennels after a successful alteration process. But Mr. Brent's maid, studying the postoperative gloom which seemed to have descended on the cat, said: "Mr. Brent —I'm afraid that cat misses himself!"

It may be well to ration yourself on trying out some of the games on these pages. Some of them take time, and you might want to take a lesson from the entomologist who was asked how his new book on insects was progressing. "It will be all right," he said, "as soon as I get the bugs out of it." And don't, whatever you do, try to do everything at once. You'll be like the nuclear physicist who had too many ions in the fire.

If anyone should try to bother you, or insist on helping you out when you're figuring out some of these twisters, insist on your own privacy, except on those occasions when you use the games for living-room havoc. With so many confessional books coming out these days, privacy has become a thing of the past. One hopeful sign of the trend being rejected was overheard in a library recently. The librarian, trying to be helpful, said to a reader: "Here's a book about a cardinal."

"No," said the reader, "I don't feel in the mood for a religious book."

The librarian quickly corrected her. "But this one is a real bird."

"I'm sorry," said the reader as she walked out the door. "I'm not interested in his private life, either."

Private or public, I hope you'll enjoy the games one way or the other, and if they can cheer up an otherwise gloomy week end, they will at least have accomplished their purpose. Gloomy week ends are pretty miserable things, as mystery writers Bill and Audrey Roos can testify.

On one liverish Sunday morning, Mrs. Roos finally summoned the courage to get out of bed and look at the weather and thermometer.

"What's it like outside?" her husband asked.

"It's gray, miserable, and forty," she answered.

"Well," said her husband as he turned over to go back to sleep, "who isn't?"

chapter one

FRACTURED INDUSTRY

Note to Game Maniacs:

At the end of each chapter, you'll find most of the games therein, ready to play and without the answers. If you are brave, you'll go to page 7 and take a shot at the games first. Then you can retreat to the reading portion of the chapter, where you'll find the answers buried amid the verbiage. If you'd like to be lazy, you can read straight through the chapter and use the game section as a memory test, or a coaster for a rum swizzle.

A JOINT CLOCK

All over this country, in this best of all possible worlds, you will find free enterprise blossoming with imaginative slogans. Although I'm a little chary about the slogan Mike Gross sent me for Reed's Flex-Arch Shoes ("Make Street Walking A Delight"), and although I certainly don't believe Alan Beck's report that there is a debt-collecting agency named Shirley, Guinness, and Murphy (Slogan: "Will Follow You All the Days of Your Life"), there are some rather fanciful companies which bear reviewing.

For instance, Edmund G. Love, the author of *Subways Are for Sleeping*, tells me his father ran an unusual retail coal business some years ago in Flint, Michigan, with a fleet of trucks marked with the legend "Love Your Coal Man." And Barbara Bromer tells me that her mother knew an undertaker named Abner Ihde, who claimed that he got a free plug at every funeral. It seems that every service always included the hymn "Ab Ihde with Me."

From Norman Hill, I learned that out in Sault Sainte Marie, Michigan, there's a law firm known as Sharp and Handy, which more or less contains a built-in slogan. From M. B.

Burkhardt, I've come up with the information that there is the Eve Transfer Company in Los Angeles with the slogan "First in Moving," and Dawn Allen advises that in New York, the Existentialist Movers carry the slogan "We Will Shoulder Your Anxiety." Another imaginative outfit I learned about is a bakery in West Springfield, Massachusetts. Margaret Bigelow tells me their slogan is: "What Foods These Morsels Be."

And some time ago, in a city I can't remember, I saw a delivery truck whisk by with the legend: "Macbeth Cleaners— Out, out, damned spot!"

Ever since that time, I've been brooding heavily on the endless opportunities for enterprise going down the drain through the failure to utilize the classics for industrial slogans. The slogans are *there*, panting and ready. The only lack is a string of companies to go with them.

Some day, for instance, somebody has got to start the Victor Refuse Company (To the Victor Belongs the Spoils). And certainly the world will be found wanting until someone comes along to create the Mercy Baby Foods Company (The Quality of Mercy Is Not Strained). Things will also be pretty dull until the Dagger Tail Light Company (Is That a Dagger I See Before Me?) is formed, to say nothing of the great vacuum which will exist until the Caesar Corn Exchange (Lend Us Your Ears) floats its common stock.

Life will be a lot brighter when the Macduff Linoleum Company (Lay On, Macduff) comes into being, and when we can get the correct time signals for the Joint Clock Company (The Time Is out of Joint).

As a matter of fact, you don't need to hold strictly to the classics for admirable slogans and companies to go with them. Bob Baker, of Cambridge, Massachusetts, tells me that he'd like to start the Pig Pen Company (You Never Run out of Oink), and Barbara Lawless is interested in investing in the Naples Chemical and Coloring Company (See Naples, and Dye).

When I mentioned my interest in this kind of ridiculous

trivia in my TRADE WINDS column, I wasn't quite prepared for the flood which would hit my RFD box with similar ideas. The exploration into the possibility of classic slogans and companies to go with them seemed to unleash some cosmic signal to drown the local post office with tears, as Shakespeare might have put it. I'm happy, though, that the strange and monstrous agony created by the twisted word and thought still brings delight to so many.

At least four correspondents sprang to action to create the Freudian Slip Company, while Richard Frohwirth went on to establish the Katz Amazing Weather-Making Service (The Fog Will Come on Little Katz's Feat). Half a dozen readers joined in unison to organize the Divinity Foundation Company (There's a Divinity Which Shapes Our Ends), while Charlotte Hutchinson went on to conjure up Dreamy Massage Oil (Ay, There's the Rub).

But this is only the start. Pauline Engel would have it known that she contemplates originating the Budd Bar and Grill (Have A Nip in the Budd), the Marriage Delicatessen (For Butter or for Wurst), and the Exclusive Parish Basement Construction Company (The Church's One Foundation).

F. Joseph Lorze is inspired to establish the Unkindest Meat Company (The Most Unkindest Cut of All), along with the Stuff Mattress Company (We Are Such Stuff as Dreams Are Made On), and the Tale Wallpaper Corporation (Thereby Hangs a Tail).

On the other hand, Carol Silverberg gets right to the point by suggesting the Laconic Weavers, Inc. (Least Said, Soonest Mended), while Mrs. Alfred Boegehold is all set to promote a new soft drink called Tummy (Drink Tummy Only with Your Ice, and I'll Drink It with Mine).

Some correspondents feel that the slogan can be dispensed with as long as the company name carries a sufficient impact. For instance, journalist Ben Hayes is threatening to take out organization papers for a company to be known as the Fail

Safe Company, to be immediately followed up by the Misery Loves Company. In addition, he's invented the Get Away From It Awl, for those who have a tendency to be butter-fingered.

Beyond all this, Gunnar Horn is about to set up a bakery to be known as the Fancy Bakers, Inc. (Tell Me Where Is Fancy Bread?)

Two other correspondents lean to the theatrical management field to organize their new enterprises. Mrs. Henry Harris wants to start the Precarious Broadway Backers Association (Where Angels Fear to Tread), and Earl Rees is ready to launch the Off-The-Hook Actor's Company (The Fault Is Not In Our Stars).

Several correspondents are rooting for the Hamlet Reducing Company (That Too, Too, Solid Flesh Will Melt), while W. A. Sparks is ready to sign stock certificates for the Sixpence Song Plugging Company (Sing A Song of Sixpence). Not satisfied with this, Mary Ellen Weiepfenning is all for starting the Scratch Cake Mix Company (I Made It Myself From Scratch).

And believe it or not, Davis Scull has a printed letterhead made up for a company known as Brillig, Tove & Slithy down in Annandale, Virginia, claiming to represent the American Worm Raisers' Association, the International Cotton Pickers Union, and the Westward Hoe Company as public relation counsel. Along with Stan McDowell of Canada, he recommends the Thankless Child Cutlery Company (How Sharper Than a Serpent's Tooth It Is to Have a Thankless Child).

Disdaining the classics, but getting right to the point, Bea Hayes wants to promote the Huff Ready-Made Dress Company (Walk Out in a Huff), while J. H. Adler makes no bones about his Sight Tranquilizers (Out Of Sight, Out Of Mind), and Look Ski Equipment (Look Before You Leap).

The list goes on, endlessly. Cornelius Lombardi is anxious to start an elevator company for your very own, personal use, to be called the Petard Elevator Company. A. L. Foss has a ready-made slogan for the Dachshund Breeders Association (Get a Long Little Doggie), to say nothing of a planned enterprise to be called the Meaning Watch Company (Every Little Meaning Has a Movement of Its Own).

And John Derr, in Tyrone, Pennsylvania, writes that he has created a special chewing gum for very angry people. "It's called Vehemint," he says, "and it could go side by side with a toothpaste I've designed which is guaranteed to ruin tooth enamel: Detrimint."

GAMES FOR CHAPTER ONE

Like most of the material in this book, this monumental tower of pleasant trivia can be used for either solitaire or group entertainment.

FOR SOLITAIRE:

Go through your battered copy of *Bartlett's Familiar Quotations* and pick out a list of memorable phrases. Or recall some of your favorite quotes from the classics, and write them down. Then try to create an enterprise to go with them. Only certain phrases will work, because there has to be full-blown double meaning with the quotation to give it the twist it needs. For instance, "Out, out damned spot!" is only good because it applies aptly to a modern cleaning establishment, yet uses the classic quotation in full.

If, for instance, you were to take Shakespeare's line "Parting is such sweet sorrow," you'll find there's not an awful lot you can do with it. You might have better luck with "Night's candles are burnt out, and jocund day stands tiptoe on the misty mountain tops"—but only a modicum. This would have to be predicated on a company called the Jocund Day Candle Company, whose chief competitor would be a company named Knight. Then their advertising could run: "Knight's Candles are burnt out—use Jocund Day."

Don't forget—we never said this was easy.

FOR GROUPS:

The best way to handle this for groups is to provide each guest with a sheet of paper listing some well-known quotations down the left-hand side of the sheet, with blank space beside them for the guests to come up with company names to go with them. It might be well to supply a list of ten quotations from above, and allow five more blank spaces for originals.

Thus, your sheets should look something like this:

SLOGAN	NAME OF COMPANY
1. To the victor belongs the spoils.	1.
2. The quality of mercy is not strained.	2.
3. Is that a dagger I see before me?	3.
4. Lend us your ears.	4.
5. Lay on, Macduff.	5.
6. There's a divinity which shapes our ends.	6.
7. Aye, there's the rub.	7.
8. The most unkindest cut of all.	8.
9. Thereby hangs a tail.	9.
10. How sharper than a serpent's tooth it is to have a thankless child.	10.
11.	11.
12.	12.
13.	13.
14.	14.
15.	15.

Score: 5 points for each industry named; 10 points for each original slogan and industry.

chapter two

LITERARY RELISH

Note to Game Maniacs:

The same process continues here as in Chapter One: If you must strain your gray matter first, turn to the game section on page 22, and try your hand at it before you turn back to the reading portion of the chapter, where you'll not only find exquisite prose, but the answers as well.

Books, authors, and titles have ganged up for a long time to provide a wide spectrum of games for insomniacs and hair-tearing hostesses. The book business is a chatty, verbal, noisy aggregate of people, and any time those in it can find an excuse to make up a game, they'll do it. For a long time, the ancient card game of "Authors" has held forth, and I assume is still popular with parents for foisting knowledge on their unsuspecting moppets.

Simply examining the customs and mores of the publishing business is a sort of a quiet, introspective game in itself. For instance, there's long been talk about what kind of book is sure to be a best seller. (Herb Caen, of the *San Francisco Chronicle*, made up his own method of making sure his books would do well. He kept them at the head of his basement stairs, so that he could say they were all on the top of the best cellar lists.) It has been a tradition in the publishing business for a long time that books about (a) Lincoln, (b) doctors, (c) dogs always are sure to have a high volume of sales. The old twister has it that one publisher decided to make assurance doubly sure and commissioned a book to be written on Lincoln's Doctor's Dog.

Beyond that, there's the famous old legend about the author who combined a lot of current high-selling ideas for a book, and brought it to his publisher to help him find a surefire title. Together, they had a long struggle. The original title, *I Made Love to a Polar Bear* seemed too weak, and the author was sent home to come up with something stronger. A week later, he came back with what he thought was a stopper: *I Made Love to a Polar Bear for the F.B.I.* But the publisher was still not satisfied, until the author came back a week later with the title: *I Made Love to a Polar Bear for the F.B.I.—and Found Romance.*

The perfect opening for a perfect best seller has long been a source of contention among the *literati*. The theory has been kicked around for a long time that you needed to get three very important elements into such a book right at the start: (a) religion, (b) royalty, (c) sex. Out of this composite came the classic opening sentence: "My God," cried the Duchess, "Get your hand off my knee!" It wasn't long after I quoted this old dog in TRADE WINDS, when Charles Degen wrote me saying that he would like to add a fourth ingredient: Mystery. Thus his guaranteed best-seller opening sentence would be:

"Holy Moses," cried the Princess, "I'm about to have a baby."

Then she smiles at the Prince and says: "I'm glad we know whodunit!"

But Helen Grace Carlisle, another correspondent, was not at all satisfied with that one. She felt that the proletariat should not be overlooked.

"My God," cried the Duchess to the plumber, "Take your hand off my knee!"

But even more appropriate in these days, she thinks, would be the sentence: "My God," cried the Duchess to the woman-dominated American male. "Take your hand off your knee and put it on mine!"

With all kinds of things to look for in and around books, you can play games with yourself for endless hours. If you've ever read book jackets (and you're bound to every time you browse in the library or bookstore), you can't help noticing how they all seem to read the same, regardless of the subject of the book. This is known in the book trade as "copywriter's anesthesia", the result of long hours of reading galleys and trying to find something fresh and new to say about them. After a long period of service in this area, I can attest that writing jacket copy can come to be a chore of crashing agony. To relieve this condition, I designed a general, all-purpose book jacket, which can adorn any book of any category for any taste, and which will allow both blurb writers and the reading public to spend the time thus saved knitting argyles, reading the book, or both:

(ANY TITLE GOES HERE)
(ANY AUTHOR'S NAME GOES HERE)

This book is wise, yes, and beautiful, too, with ugly and sinister overtones. It is at once shocking and soothing—a book with lusty virility, bursting with compassion and pity. Its utter simplicity is equalled only by its stirring complexity which will leave the reader emotionally exhausted as it replenishes his deep spiritual needs.

To say that it is at once adult and mature is to ignore its refreshing naive appeal to children and sado-masochists. Within its carefully wrought lines are the seeds of tenderness which at last reveal a mood of enlightened horror and depressive joy.

Its daring, lurid, brash, and provocative approach to sex has been watered down, but not too much. Its majestic turbulence pragmatically states its theme with finely etched precision.

> (Author's name here) is a writer of extreme sensibility
> whose rough, masterful style bluntly spells out delicate
> understanding and stimulating puzzlement. His flashes
> of quiet insight and outspoken integrity deviously com-
> bine to make a moving, absorbing, detached, hilarious,
> and tragic picture told with peerless subjective objec-
> tivity.

But it's good for the reading public to remember that publishers have their problems. In addition to being faced with a
finite quantity of adjectives to describe their wares, there are
also books which resist titles to describe them. Whitney Dar-
row, Jr., the cartoonist, tells about the time he discovered
Peter Schwed at Simon & Schuster groaning about the trouble he was having in finding a good title for a collection of
stories about famous sportsmen and their accomplishments.
"The only title that really fits," said Schwed, "is one that we
can't use—*Athletes' Feats.*"

Vance Packard once told me that he was sure that publishers
were becoming so depressed that their moods were being un-
erringly reflected in the books they were publishing. He
pointed out that at one time, every title in a Book-of-the-
Month Club advertisement seemed to be steeped in morbid-
ity. In a single ad he noticed:

The Edge of Sadness, *The* Agony *and the Ecstasy, The
Rise and* Fall *of the Third Reich, To Kill a Mockingbird, The
Coming* Fury, *A Matter of Life and Death, The Winter of
our* Discontent, *The King Must Die, The* Last *of the Just,
The* Decline *and* Fall *of the Roman Empire, Who* Killed
Society?

About the only cheerful titles in the BOMC list at that
time were: *Ideal Marriage,* followed logically, of course, by
Dr. Spock Talks to Mothers.

And look at some of the letters publishers get. Grove Press
received a letter from a reader who had just finished reading
Jou Pu Tuan, the seventeenth-century erotic classic. Said the

letter: "This book took me into so many Chinese boudoirs that I began to feel like a Peking Tom."

What's more, Fred Kerner of Hawthorn Books, tells me that his publishing chores require his handling authors who bring him bizarre plots of all kinds. One of them came to him with an idea for a modernized adult western. In this version, the outlaws beat the stage coach rap, but the withholding tax makes them live in abject poverty.

Almost everywhere you look, someone is trying to get into the publishing act. I passed a tire dealer not long ago, who labeled his new and used tires: "Friction" and "Non-Friction." In addition, a whole new phase in publishing is being developed for soft-cover books. Those in limp leather, of course, will be made from *very* relaxed cows. The cheapest form of books will be called Pauper Backs; those with sexy covers, Peeper Backs, and those with a special low price for Scotsmen, Piper Backs.

Even religious publishers have their problems. The same Mike Gross who lent me the intelligence about the shoes which make streetwalking a delight, tells me about a father whose young son kept coming home from Sunday School every week with a large, illustrated picture representing one of the ten commandments. These were issued by a religious publisher who was intent on illustrating every sort of abstract idea for the young mind to grasp. The first week, the child came home with a picture card for the first commandment, showing a graven image crossed out with a large X. The next weeks followed suit, with various illustrations attempting to illustrate honoring one's parents, forbidding false witness, stealing, and so forth.

The father said he waited with bated breath for the ninth week, which dealt with the delicate subject of adultery. But without fail, the youngster showed up at home with a full-color picture card showing a sneaky milkman pouring water into a bucket full of pure, whole milk.

But this kind of thing could go on forever.

All we can hope is that none of this will be repeated at a literary cocktail party, which everyone knows is a fête worse than death.

Book critics, however, and not publishers, are those who start us off on our first official game in this category. Critics are not necessarily a surly lot, they just act that way. There isn't an author living who doesn't claim that a bad review is the direct result of what the critic had for breakfast in the morning.

Critics also have a bad habit of seizing on memorable phrases, many of which are snatched up by eager publishers to decorate their book advertising. These phrases have stimulated the game *Fractured Book Reviews*.

FRACTURED BOOK REVIEWS

The trick here is to see how many fictional critic's quotes you can make for a list of unlikely books that may cross your mind in a weak moment. Like most of the games in this book, it is good for either solitaire or group noodling, as they say on Madison Avenue. And if you should happen to get hooked with this sort of nonsense, it's entirely your own responsibility.

Examples might include:

The Telephone Directory:	Too many characters.
Webster's Dictionary:	Too wordy.
Hammond's Atlas:	Covers too much ground.
Dun & Bradstreet Report:	Deserves a lot of credit.
Bulletin of the U.S.	
Revenue Service:	Taxing.
The Works of Plato:	Good dialog.
Euclid's Geometry:	Only for squares.
Tiffany's Catalog:	Has a hollow ring.

The response to this from various *Saturday Review* readers was immediate and heartening. Among the choice items were:

The Check Book: (H. Van Gelder)	Elusive . . . something missing . . . fades away at the end.
Fanny Farmer Cookbook: (Mrs. D. H. Tyler)	Enriching.
Handbook of Adhesives: (J. L. Van Name)	Couldn't put it down.
New Haven Timetable: (Virginia Ott)	Not true to life.

Later, at a gathering of a facile group of wagsters, the game moved ahead to entirely new depths. Sitting above the salt were television's Henry Morgan, Paul Alter, Gil Fates, and the doleful and famous Allen Sherman. (Actually, all were above the salt, because someone had left it at one end of the table.)

Suggestions flew at such a pace that it was impossible to preserve all but the following:

The Story of Cotton:	Highly absorbing.
Burpee's Seed Catalog:	Grows on you.
Dow-Jones Report:	Average.
The Surgeon's Manual:	Had me in stitches.
Audubon's Bird Guide:	Doesn't dovetail.
Fail-Safe:	Great combination.

The gathering came to a merciful end when Mr. Alter said: "Has anyone read *Dissertation on a Roast Lamb*—by Charles Pig?"

The game, of course, has endless variations. You can take, as I did in a weak moment, a batch of any contemporary titles from a library list, and come up with a few apt, one-line reviews for the questionable convenience of your friends:

Cyril Connolly's *Previous Convictions:*	Plenty of hard cell.
Richard Condon's *An Infinity of Mirrors:*	No reflection on the author.

Alex Austin's	
The Blue Guitar:	Left me unstrung.
Ray Chandler's	
Killer in the Rain:	Every lethal bit counts.
Agatha Christie's	
The Clocks:	The villain gets the works.
Catherine Gavin's	
The Fortress:	Starts off with a bang.
Max Shulman's	
Anyone Got A Match:	Striking.

It's bad enough to be plagued by this game as a solitary effort, but if you should want to foist it on your friends, a suggested form is supplied at the end of the chapter, if you'll agree to forego all responsibility for its use.

BOOK CONVERSATION

Allied closely to Fractured Book Reviews is a hammock game which John Porter, the sports car racer, says sprung up at his summer home in Lime Rock, Connecticut.

"It's an insufferable game," says Mr. Porter, "and can produce unlimited groans of agony."

The idea is to take a book or author and piece it together with a cliché which plays off the title or name. For instance:

"Have you read C. P. Snow?"
   "No—I couldn't plow through him."
"Have you read *The Good Earth?*"
   "Yes, but I didn't dig it."
"Have you read *The Leopard?*"
   "Yes, but I found it spotty." ·
"Have you read Dorothy Parker's *Enough Rope?*"
   "No, I just skipped through it."

"It's the surest way I know," concludes Mr. Porter, "of preventing a guest from overstaying his visit."

This game can be played in the same manner as Fractured

Book Reviews, with the same type of sheet to keep score. Or, you can simply sit around the living room and bat it back and forth. A considerate hostess might make it a point to hand out tranquillizers after the first fifteen minutes, if you last that long.

OTHER VARIATIONS ON A THEME

By now you must be convinced that books bring out the worst in all of us. But the end is not in sight, as these additional self-inflicted ideas will testify:

Subject Matter

This game is the result of the efforts of several insomniacs in their attempt to get to sleep on a hot August night when the air conditioning went off. The idea, if you can call it that, is to take a highly unlikely subject matter, and apply it to a title, or at least an approximation of a title, of an actual book. If this confuses you, be a little patient, because you will be more confused before this is over.

It was Silas Spitzer, food editor of *Holiday*, who came up with the idea for a book about a restaurant which served very miserable food. The title: *The Salad of the Bad Café*.

But correspondent Nancy Tooney has some ideas of her own, equally dolorous:

1. The memoirs of a dragon who devoured a member of King Arthur's Round Table: (*Tender Is the Knight*)
2. The latest epistle from the Vatican: (*The Bull from the See*)
3. The story of a scooter shop featuring vehicles for neurotics: (*The Oedipus Cycle*)

Again, Miss Tooney is not alone. She is joined by John O'Brien, a gentleman of Malden, Massachusetts, who tells me there ought to be a book about a little boy who always gets up when his father's alarm goes off (*The Son Also*

Rises) and another one about a man caught in a meat grinder (*A Farewell to Arms*).

Peter Windsor joins the chorus with a compact library of his own:

(1) The biography of a name dropper (*The Ycleptomaniac*)

(2) A gourmet's memoirs (*Nobody Knows the Truffles I've Seen*)

(3) The story of a nervous caterer (*His Eye Is on the Spare Roe*)

(4) The story of a nervous usher (*His Eye Is on the Spare Row*)

If you think these are bad, take a look at those which the following literary acrobats have sent in:

From R. B. Wallace:

The biography of a successful drugstore clerk (*Dristan, and I Sold 'er*)

From Marcia Ringel:

The story of a grocery store proprietor who never could keep an inventory on hand (*The Joint Is Out of Thyme*)

From David Batterson:

A tribute to a modern American artist (*Hail, O Dali!*)

From Charles Heilmann:

A book about a saintly Maryland prelate (*Baltimore Aureole*)

From Chuck Alverson:

Confessions of a dope addict (*Gone to Pot*)

From Allan Kalmus:

A travel book about island hopping in Hawaii (*Here Today, Gone to Maui*)

From Louise Lawrence:

A book about government workers in office jobs (*Swivel Service Today*)

From Nancy Tuttle:

A book about Rembrandt van Rijn's favorite Belgian Shepherd (*Rijn Tijn Tijn*)

From David Bernstein:

A redundant book to get across the point (*I Was a Teen-Age Adolescent*)

From Nancy Baker:

An unclassified book, defying analysis (*I Was a Teen-Age Geriatric*)

The last book really doesn't qualify, but it gives us an excuse to bring this mayhem to a merciful end. For the benefit of those masochists who would like to try their hands at this, either singly or in a literary wolf-pack, there's a form provided in the game section which includes everything but the aspirin tablets.

There are other variations, too, but they don't exactly make up any kind of a game. For instance, Jules Feiffer, the unhampered wit, cartoonist, and commentator, one time explored, in a cartoon sequence in the *Village Voice,* the idea of writing songs to go with the titles of new books. Some of the staggering possibilities for ballad writers he came up with are: "Franny and Zooey Were Sweethearts," "I Lost My Heart at the Tropic of Cancer," and "Calories Don't Count—But You Do."

Other suggestions which have come our way are: "Let Me Be Your Queen, King Rat," "I Fell in Love with You When I Learned You Were a Rothschild," and "What's the Pitch, Catch-22?"

Although James Jones's *From Here to Eternity* could stand as a title in its own right, the song from which it is taken is the subject of a riddle that columnist Herb Caen also sent along: "What has twelve feet, feathers, and goes 'Ba-Ba-Ba'?" The answer, of course, is six Indians singing the Whiffenpoof song.

And some misguided souls get themselves in a trap by try-ing to invent new titles for record albums to replace such platters as: "Music to Relax With," "Music to Slumber By," "Music to Live By"—the list goes on endlessly. Here are a few suggestions which we pass along gratuitously to album makers:

"Music to Neutralize the Beatles With"; "Music to Break the Tedium of the Long Island Railroad By"; "Music to Keep Your Wife Quiet for a Short Period of Time, Sort Of"; "Music to Offset the Effects of Extra-Dry Martinis, for the Most Part"; "Music to Keep Hi-Fi Fanatics From Blasting You, During."

And there is always the album "The Cossack Chorus Sings Just for You," if none of these suit your fancy.

And before we drop the subject of titles altogether, with a sickening thud, I hope, there's one comment worth passing along. A customer was browsing through the book version of the play "Oh, Dad, Poor Dad, Mother's Hung You in the Closet and I'm Feelin' So Sad," in a bookstore. He was over-heard to say: "Well, I finished the play, but I haven't had time to get through the title."

GAMES FOR CHAPTER TWO

Rules: Make up quick, short book review quotations for the following titles. Five spaces are provided for your own books and reviews. Score: Five points for each review for listed title accepted by the group. Ten points for each acceptable original title and review. Example: *The Telephone Directory.* Too many characters . . .

BOOK TITLE	CRITIC'S REVIEW
1. *Dun & Bradstreet Report*	1.
2. *Handbook of Adhesives*	2.
3. *The Story of Cotton*	3.
4. *Burpee's Seed Catalog*	4.
5. *Dow Jones Report*	5.
6. *The Surgeon's Manual*	6.
7. *Hammond's Atlas*	7.
8. *Webster's Dictionary*	8.
9. *Audubon's Bird Guide*	9.
10.	10.
11.	11.
12.	12.
13.	13.
14.	14.
15.	15.

TOTAL SCORE:——

SUBJECT MATTER

Fill in opposite the correct number a fractured book title to go with the subject matter described as an unlikely book. Score: 5 points for each fractured book title; 10 points for each original subject matter and title. Example: Memoirs of a dragon who devoured a member of King Arthur's Round Table. *Tender Is the Knight* by F. Scott Fitzgerald.

SUBJECT MATTER	TITLE (Author listed as clue)
1. Latest epistle from the Vatican	1. (Ernest Hemingway)
2. Boy who gets up when his father's alarm goes off	2. (Ernest Hemingway)
3. A man is caught in a meat grinder	3. (Ernest Hemingway)
4. Tribute to a modern American artist	4. (Song from David Merrick musical)
5.	5.
6.	6.
7.	7.
8.	8.
9.	9.
10.	10.

TOTAL SCORE:——

chapter three

FUN YOU CAN HAVE WITH WORDS

Note to Game Maniacs:

If you would like to dive directly into the self-torturing game section here, turn to page 34 of this chapter and eat your heart out. For answers, then refer back to the reading portion of the chapter.

I received a letter one time from Henry Malone, professor of history at Georgia State College, relating a very poignant story. A missionary in the jungles was seized by a tribe of cannibals, tied to a post, and jabbed with daggers and spears so that the savages could drink his blood. After a week of this gruesome ordeal, he looked the Chief squarely in the eye and said: "Look—I'm tired of being stuck for the drinks."

Since his protest was so mild, it is obvious that this man was a masochist, but certainly no worse a one than those thousands of people who like to make up and figure out games with words. Some people even do it instinctively, like the scholar who asked a bartender for a Martinus.

"Beg your pardon, sir," said the bartender, "but you mean a Martini, don't you?"

"Look, sir," said the scholar, "if I want two, I'll ask for them."

Another man, according to publicist Stan Warren, was enjoying the opening of a bar at a New York theater shortly after these institutions were permitted to serve liquor during intermission. He beamed at the rest of the theater-going crowd and said: "This is the greatest bourbon renewal project of 'em all!"

You simply cannot stop people from playing with words. If they don't do it directly, they do it indirectly. Like the Madison Avenue account executive who died, and whose boss was asked: "What did he have?"

"Well," said the boss, "he had General Foods, American Tobacco, and Revlon. . . ."

Of course, they're always fooling with words on Madison Avenue. Where else would they think of that delicate definition for Death: "It's Nature's way of telling us to 'slow down.'"

Even doctors fool around with words. There was a doctor I once heard about who was an avid horseback rider, and he liked to leave his office occasionally to go riding. He felt guilty, however, about asking his answering service to tell a lie. With inspired imagination, he named his horse "Consultation," so that the answering service could simply say: "I'm sorry, but the doctor is out on Consultation."

Words have a way of catching up with people, however. A gentleman made the mistake of writing to the Publisher's Clearing House to ask them why he had received a duplicate bill. The elucidating explanation he received said, in part:

"This is the card that causes a bill to be sent to you automatically each month. Because we didn't find it and pull it out of file, you'll continue to get bills, even though you paid . . . You will receive still another bill from us in a week or so. When it arrives just send the whole thing back to us—the outside envelope, the letter, the bill form, and especially the reply envelope inside. Each piece is a clue to where your card is hiding . . . Please do not send back any bill that arrived *before* this letter reaches you. Just wait a bit. If no bill at all arrives, you'll know we didn't make an error, and all is well. But if a bill comes *after* this letter that is the one we'd like you to send back."

What's more, if you start fooling around with words,

you're going to get mixed up with puns, and from then on in, everything is your own fault. If you want to get technical, the fifty-dollar name for pun is *paronomasia*. This sounds like a disease, and it really is.

When you succumb to it, you run into things like this:

– A letter writer, intent on getting information from a garden magazine, who signs himself: Constant Weeder.

– A college president, who warns his alumni fund chairman against asking for too much money at one time: "Don't put all your begs in one asking."

– A gangster who stood by at a gangland funeral: "They shouldn't put all those yeggs in one casket."

– The Madrid bus driver, who yelled: "I don't want all you Basques in one exit."

– The philosopher who wanted to leave his wife, but he kept putting Descartes before divorce.

– The dog who decided to cooperate with a psychologist, who said: "I'm falling in, Pavlov, with you."

– The baseball pitcher with a sore arm, in the throws of agony.

– The transcendentalist, who worked only on upper plates.

– The touring prophet, who was a sight-seer.

– And, back to Madison Avenue again, the account executive who bought himself a new sincere-sucker suit.

It should be obvious to anyone that words get you into trouble. Even teen-agers are susceptible. A lady named Mary Reay had been waiting a good many weeks before the pictures she ordered from Tokyo finally reached her. When they did, her daughter remarked: "I knew some day your prints would come along."

And Irving Gitlin, the executive producer at NBC-TV responsible for the White Paper series, has won many awards both with this network and with CBS-TV when he was there. But an associate of his remarked: "These awards have simply brought a plaque on both your houses." This of course is no worse than the comment made by Allan Kalmus, who suggests that the next long-range launching from Cape Kennedy will be an Intra-Venus shot. And certainly no worse than the suggestion made for a new magazine about Dalmatians: *Spots Illustrated*. About the only cure for people who persist in this kind of thing is to send them away to be pummelled in that Egyptian school for masseurs, where the disciplinarians are called Cairo-proctors.

The games, if you can call them that, which follow are an assorted lot. If you care to tackle them, it will be—as the tomb maker said, nobody's vault but your own. If you fail, you may fall into the category of the description of a friend overheard on a Fifth Avenue bus: "Way down deep—she's shallow." Or if you succeed, you may want to retire from this sort of nonsense forever.

ANIMAL CRACKERS

We may as well start off with animals. A little like the Quaker who was heading north with a dog team. "My dogs are working like Friends," he said. Or perhaps like that famous but durable old-timer about the zoo keeper who created a crossbreed between a tiger and a parrot. You may recall what he said when they asked him what kind of a creature came out of that combination: "I don't know—but when he talks, we *listen*." Or even like the dog who sat on the chicken roost and created pooched eggs. You see how this sort of thing keeps on going, once it's started. There's little or no cure.

When Earle Reynolds and his family, Barbara, Ted and Jessica, were anchored off Hiroshima in the famous yacht "Phoenix," they invented a game calculated to take the curse off the work of swabbing the decks and polishing the bright work. For the want of a better word, we're calling it *Animal Crackers*, although there is certainly no law against your making up your own title, like *Platypus Rex*.

The concept is simple; the execution of it a little more difficult. The main idea is to take an animal characteristic, or a descriptive word about the animal which turns out to have a meaning all its own.

For instance:

- as overbearing as a rabbit
- as inflamed as a moth
- as hidebound as a rhino
- as canny as a sardine
- as testy as a guinea pig
- as earthy as a worm
- as foul-minded as a chicken
- as chaste as a fox
- a gambler, like a lamb
- as instinctive as a skunk

It's hard to shut this sort of thing off, once it starts. You may end up, as Mr. Reynolds suggests:

- in a splinter group, with the woodpeckers
- an undercover agent with the bed bugs

Or you may turn out to be:

- a spitting image of a llama

As Mr. Reynolds also points out, it's hardly necessary to be as detailed as a manx cat. He and his family have already determined that:

- turtles are self-contained
- pigs are hamstrung
- hedgehogs are oddballs
- starfish are radiant
- blowfish are swell
- molluscs are extremely shellfish
- a whale is a blowhard
- a mole, subversive
- yeast germ, inbred
- an adder, calculating
- a canary, jaundiced

There is simply no way of stopping the Reynolds family. They go on to claim that they've discovered:

- the approved seal
- the baggy crocodile
- the truncated elephant
- the busy lion (the lion is always busy)
- the boring termite
- the manta ray, a good skate

Cross-Breed

Apparently inspired by the zoo keeper who crossed the tiger with the parrot, Dr. Joseph Schechner tells me about the game his children invented to keep him awake at nights. With the fiendish proclivity children have for torturing parents, the youngsters have developed animal names with the last letters or syllable of one being the first syllable or the first letters of the second animal:

- The otterrier
- The zebrat
- The seal-ion
- The hippopotamuskrat
- The ermink
- The elephantelope
- The kangorooster
- The buffalobster
- The weaselephant

If these animals were ever assembled in one zoo, we're sure the chorus would be un-bearable.

The Inverted Zoo

For a long time, I had been brooding about the canary who painted his cage people-yellow, or the turtle who was wearing a man-necked sweater. When I mentioned this in my column, a good many readers joined in the game, with these happy results:

- Whales that had a people of a good time
- Ducks with people bumps
- a boy-footed bear
   (From Sadelle Hershey)
- a human-hearted lion
   (From Elizabeth Nitchie)
- the female whale with a corset of lady-bones
   (From Norman Davis)
- the hog who spoke a lot of man-wash
   (From Harry Ober)
- the sardines who felt like people in the subway
   (From Norma Neaderthal)
- the cat who let the man out of the bag
   (From Suzanne Suskin)

These would make up a tidy zoo for anyone, and I'm sure you'll be able to add to the list.

Speaking Zoologically

Up in the quiet village of Newfields, N.H., the Reverend and Mrs. E. F. Stoneham have conjured up a game which is just as frightful as any of the others. "The rules are obvious, and can be changed at will," the good reverend comments —and you'll probably wish you could change them when you lie awake trying to figure out more like these:

- Pelican-tankerously
- kangaroo-fully
- rabbit-terly
- chickadee-ply
- whippoorwill-fully
- giraffe-ably
- elephant-tastically
- nightingale-ly

- leopard-onably
- beaver-bosely
- hamster-nly
- badger-mainly

"Good as a time killer?" Reverend Stoneham asks. Yes, we might add, if it doesn't kill you first.

Pigeons

Dorothy Drucker, of New York, was free to confess that she has been intrigued by the "intellectual soporifics" readers have sent in, and has developed her own analgesic which is to parody Gertrude Stein's "Pigeons on the Grass, alas!":

- Pigeons on the floor
  Quoth the raven "Nevermore."

- Pigeons on the fence,
  No sense.

- Pigeons overhead,
  'Nuff said!

Not content with pigeons alone, she goes on to supply a new subject for Gertrude Stein's original:

- Ducks on the grass,
  Alack, quack, quack

- Barefoot on the grass?
  Alas! Glass!

To seal off (no pun intended) the whole animal business forever, there is the story that John Ross tells about the time he tried to sneak into a prehistoric animal exhibit at a museum, along with a friend. "Unfortunately, we were caught," he says. "The icthyosaurus."

GAMES FOR CHAPTER THREE

ANIMAL CRACKERS

Take an animal characteristic—or a descriptive word about the animal, and turn it into a meaning all its own. Example: As *overbearing* as a rabbit.

1. As ——— as a moth
2. As ——— as a rhino
3. As ——— as a sardine
4. As ——— as a guinea pig
5. As ——— as a worm
6. As ——— as a chicken
7. As ——— as a fox
8. A ———, like a lamb
9. As ——— as a skunk

Now associate these animals with a double-meaning characteristic or group:

1. In a ——— group, with the woodpeckers
2. An ——— agent with the bed bugs
3. A ——— image of a llama

Find a double meaning descriptive adjective for these animals. Example: Turtles are *self-contained*.

1. Pigs are ———
2. Hedgehogs are ———
3. Starfish are ———
4. Blowfish are ———

5. Molluscs are extremely ——
6. A whale is a ——
7. A mole is ——
8. A yeast germ is ——
9. An adder is ——
10. A canary is ——

Find more adjectives with double meanings to apply to these animals. Example: The *approved* seal.

1. The —— crocodile
2. The —— elephant
3. The —— lion
4. The —— termite
5. The manta ray, a —— ——

ANSWERS ON PAGES 30 AND 31

CROSS-BREED

See how many amusing new animals you can create by combining the last letter or syllable of one animal with the first syllable or first letters of the other. Example: The hippopotamuskrat.

Excellent   8
Good   6
Fair   5
Poor   3

ANSWERS ON PAGE 31—Add three points for your own originals not included in answers.

THE INVERTED ZOO

How many expressions can you find to invert to get an amusing switch of animals and people. Example: The canary who painted his cage people-yellow; the turtle wearing a man-necked sweater.

Excellent   7
Good   5
Fair   3

ANSWERS ON PAGE 32—Add three points for your originals not
included in answers.

SPEAKING ZOOLOGICALLY

How many animals and adverbs can you combine to get
amusing phrases, like Pelican-tankerously.

Excellent   10
Good   7
Fair   5

ANSWERS ON PAGES 32 AND 33—Add three points for your originals.

chapter four

MORE FUN WITH WORDS— ONOMATOPOETIC DIVISION

Note to Game Maniacs:

As usual, the pure game portion of this chapter is found at the end, on page 47. The reading portion of the chapter is always available for you to sneak a look at.

It all started when a film editor from New York by the name of John Teeple dropped me a line saying that he was kept awake nights wondering why so many words beginning with the letters *sn* are related in some way to the general area of the nose and mouth.

A quick rundown of some of the words indicated that he had hit on something: snort, snout, snoot, sniff, snorkel, snicker, sneeze, snippy, snore, sneer, snide, snoop, snob, snivel, snarl, snub, snuff, snuffle. Although the etymological explanation seemed undetermined, I later received so much mail on this that a book could be written on the subject. I would almost be willing to say that etymology could outrank sex any day.

Many readers of the column indicated independently that thinking up new associations was the perfect cure for insomnia. This is not to say that insomnia, like sin, is something always to be against. I once knew a professor who was so interesting that the entire class had insomnia.

I learned later, also, from Paul Schlueter at Minnesota State College that John B. Lord's book *Experiments in Diction*,

Rhetoric and Style (Rinehart, 1955) demonstrates that words beginning with *wr* seem to involve twisting, and of course could easily be applied to the sacroiliacal dance of the same name: wrangle, wrinkle, wrestle, wrench, wrest, wriggle, wreathe, wring. (This, as a matter of fact, makes up a perfect definition of the dance.)

The same book indicates that words beginning in *b* are often associated with the feeling of roundness, or an extension of something round: belly, billow, ball, bulk, bulge, boil, bubble, to name a few.

Among the most popular were the associations with words beginning with *gl* (glare, glitter, glint, glow, etc), indicating brightness or light. But at the same time, one correspondent wrote that words beginning with the same consonants indicated just the opposite (glum, gloom, glower). For one correspondent, words beginning with *sh* indicate motion (shake, shimmy, shrug, shudder); for another the same consonants mean repression (shut, shunt, shelve).

Qu seems to mean subdue to some (quash, quiet, quell) and uneasy to another (quake, quail, quaver). But many agreed that the letter *l* takes us right back to sex again: lewd, licentious, lascivious, lecherous, libertine, lustful, libidinous. Even an eighth grade class, of all things, landed on this association.

Several respondents took exception to associating words beginning with *fl* with graceful, light movement (flowing, fluid, flying). They looked at it in just the opposite way (flop, flank, flat).

And one professor notes that he has proof that words such as this have nothing whatever to do with graceful movement:

"For 318 of our first semester students in English composition," he writes, "the initial gambit of *fl* connotes something remote from this meaning. They *fl*unked!"

For the benefit of future generations who might want to writhe, wrestle, and wriggle with this sort of thing, we list the efforts of this stalwart group of etymologists:

From Gladys Cutler:

(*B* is for babies)

- birth
- bassinet
- bottle
- blanket
- burp
- bunting
- bib
- buggy
- bonnet
- bawl
- bootee
- bye-bye

From Edwin Goodwin:

(*Sq* is for crushing action)

- squirt
- squint
- squash
- squelch
- squeeze

From James Churchyard:

(*Fl* is for lightness and grace)

- float
- flit
- fluid
- flight
- fly
- flee
- fluffy
- flimsy

(Also, *sp* is for forceful, outward movement)

- splash
- spume
- spit
- spray
- sputter
- spurt

Mr. Churchyard adds that if enough of these sounds had inherent meanings, we might well be on our way toward a subconscious universal language.

Curtis C. Page, professor of English at Drake University, challenges Mr. Churchyard, however. He and his Freshman English class take sides with the ungainly school: flip, flop, flutter, flap, flounder, flog, flinch, flicker, flare, flatten, fluster, flood, flunk, flim-flam, fluke, flabby, flatulent, flaw, flagrant, flabbergast. ("Graceful, indeed!" says Curtis Page.)

From Alice Bernheim:

  (*Tr* is for travel)

- trip
- traipse
- tramp
- trot
- trunk
- train
- trek
- trail

  (Also, *cr* is for unpleasant sounds)

- crack
- crunch
- crackle
- creak
- crank
- crick
- crash
- croak

From Ann Agranoff:

  (*St* is for lack of movement)

- stop
- stationary
- stay
- still
- stall
- stilted

From Peter Finston and Thomas Chappell:

  (*Gl* means light)

- glare
- glisten
- glaze
- glitter
- gleam
- glory
- gleed
- glister
- glimmer
- gloss
- glint
- glow

From Sharon Arkin, Thomas Cramer, and Victor Schwab:

  (*L* is depraved or highly sexed!)

- lewd
- lustful
- licentious
- leering
- lascivious
- libidinous
- lecherous

From Claudia Gaines:

  (*Wh* is for the rush of air or breath)

- whiff
- whisper
- whistle
- wheeze

– whine	– whip
– whimper	– whir
– whizz	– whirl

From John L. Cole:
  (*Sw* is for graceful motion)

– swing	– swan
– sway	– swallow
– swell	– sweep
– swivel	– swim
– swoon	– swirl

  (But *sw* also means more violent motion)

– swack	– swipe
– swag	– swashbuckler
– swat	– switch
– swagger	– swoosh

From Rose L. Cocks:
  (*Obs* is unpleasant)

– obscene	– obstinate
– obstacle	– obsequious
– obscure	– obsolete

From Joey Rothschild and Tooni Gordi:
  (*Gr*, invented by dogs, is out of sorts, harsh, and unpleasant)

– gruff	– gripe
– growl	– gross
– grouch	– groggy
– grate	– grapple
– gravel	– grab
– grist	– grimy
– gristle	– grimace
– grunt	– groan
– grim	– grumble
– grumpy	– grind

- grasping   - gritty
- grubby   - grafter
- grueling   - grifter
- grisly   - grief
- grizzly   - greed
- grovel   - grudge
- gruesome   - grave

She would also know, parenthetically, if there is more than one English word that ends in *lct* other than "mulct."

From Nannette Jay:

(*Qu* is unpleasant)

- quail   - queer
- quake   - querulous
- qualm   - quibble
- quarrel   - quietus
- quaver   - quiver
- queasy

(Also, *sl* is for mire)

- slime   - slog
- slop   - slosh
- sludge   - slough
- slippery   - sluice
- slither   - sluit
- slobber   - slush

(And: *y* is for sounds, as is *wh*)

- yawn   - yelp
- yap   - yodel
- yip   - yammer
- yawk   - yabber*
- yell

(And: *sh* is for reduction in size)

- shred   - shrink
- shrimp   - shrivel

* She adds that she is not a Swede.

The eighth grade class at Post Junior High School in Detroit not only joined others in the licentious connotations of the innocent letter *l*, but came up with several others:

Sc is for irritating sounds: screech, scrape, scratchy, scream.

Sl is for dirt and untidiness: slop, slush, slum, slime, slew, sleazy, slosh, slovenly.

From Ina Forbus: *thr* means violent motion. Thrash, thresh, thrust, throttle, throw, threaten, throe.

From Mary Lou Meese and Emily Cassebeer, *kn* is knotty, and *str* is forceful. Knee, kneed, knickers, knuckles, knobby, knell, knurl. "A little far fetched," they write, "but if a knee is really a knot, then knit can be included because knitting is essentially knotting a knot." From the point of view of *str*: strict, stringent, strident, strength, straight.

Theron E. Coffin, who has taught English at East Orange, N. J. High School for 34 years, finds a variety of patterns with *sl*: (1) Slender objects—slat, slice, sliver, slit, slot. (2) Smoothness—sleek, slick, slippery, slip, slide, slither. (3) Craftiness—sly, slink. (4) Dull or careless persons—slack, sluggish, slouchy, slatternly, slug, slob, slut.

To Leota Keir, another English teacher, *cl* has a couple of meanings. (1) The sound of collision—clang, clatter, clump, clap, clash, clip, click, clammer, clog, clackety, clank. (2) Housework—clean, clothes, clothespins, clutter, clear, closets, climb, clock.

Bertha Berman compounds the whole situation with her observation that the letter *h* not only connotes haste or confusion in most cases, but also seems to be the constant victim of compound *rhyming* words: hum-drum, harum-scarum, helter-skelter, hurdy-gurdy, hurry-scurry, hustle-bustle, hodge-podge, hocus-pocus, hoity-toity, hob-nob, hurly-burly, hoi-polloi, and for good measure, hi-fi.

Many respondents probed the significance of all this in depth. Carol Waters examines the possibility that when a vowel sound is thin, produced with the mouth nearly shut, the words will most often be of the bright, happy sort; while those with vowels which require a rounded sound are heavier, darker, more orotund. Some Chinese friends of hers have pointed out that this is generally the case with the words in the various Chinese dialects.

"The *br* words serve to illustrate my point," she writes. "For on the one hand we have such bright, tight words as bright, brisk, brittle, and—in contrast—are brusque, broad, brood."

Novelist Guy Endore has written a novel *Detour at Night* which is full of sounds with built-in meanings, and writes me that Hans Joachim Stoerig, who undertook the German translation of the book was able to find German equivalents for all the word-play in the book—suggesting again the universal language idea. And Frank C. Baxter, Professor Emeritus of English at the University of Southern California, points out that an Englishman named Macdonald Critchley published a book in 1939 which added a new theory of language origins to the old suggested theories of bow-wow, pooh-pooh, ding-dong sorts that are to be found in all the books dealing with language or origin.

"Critchley suggests that language began as a sort of vocal gesture and that all languages retain vestiges of this.

"For instance, words meaning thin, attenuated, narrow and sharp seem to be on the pattern of needle, steeple, teeny-weeny, *aiguille, fils*, etc. Many words dealing with food seem almost a veritable pointing at the pharynx and the oesophagus: gullet, gorge, grub, gourmet, gourmand, chow, gulp, etc. The very act of saying words like the following suggests an enclosed space: womb, tomb, *chambre*, room, etc. So you see that a formal psychologist has seen these phenomena as something more than coincidental."

Of even greater scope is the interest in onomatopoeia of researchers in DNA and cancer, we learned from Dr. Robert D. Barnard.

"The process goes far beyond the specific descriptive examples furnished in your column," he wrote me. "It has become such an important part of a new scientific subdiscipline, biologic information theory, that with due acknowledgement to many unsung contributors who have worked in this area, Mr. Churchyard is correct . . . The subconscious universal language is actually that of DNA, the 'genetic substance,' a spiral or double-stranded helix which, when unfurled, is for all the world like a magnetic recording tape and will cause the re-emission of 'noises' originally impressed on that tape if played in a suitable reproducing system."

Dr. Barnard goes on to discuss the deductive decipherment of the DNA code, then adds: "There is, nevertheless, another approach; it is an inductive approach on which many people are working. And in that regard, I must warn Mr. Churchyard about the consequences of his own temerity, and your own column of its ill-advised action in having *sp*illed the beans prematurely."

On top of this impressive analysis, another professor is interested in examining these examples on an IBM 650 computer. All this may add up to the fact that for the first time, having fun with words might make a contribution to science.

But Scott Corbett might well sum up the matter in another light: "If words beginning in *wr* seem to involve twisting," he writes, "how about writing itself, that twisting, twisted task from which the wretched, wriggling writer finds no wre-lease?"

GAMES FOR CHAPTER FOUR

Game #1

How many single, double or triple letters can you find which begin a series of words, all of which have similar meanings? (Example: *Sn* relates to nose and mouth: Snicker, snort, snout, snoot, sniff, etc.) Each series should have at least four related words. DO NOT LOOK AT THE GAMES BELOW THIS BEFORE ATTEMPTING GAME #1.

Excellent 12
Good   9
Fair   6

ANSWERS ON PAGE 40 THROUGH 46—Add three points for originals.

Game #2

Without consulting a dictionary, how many words can you list relating to babies, beginning with the letter *B*?

Excellent 10
Good   7
Fair   5

Under the same conditions, how many words can you relate to a crushing action, beginning with the letters *Sq*?

Excellent 4
Good   3
Fair   2

Under similar conditions, how many words can you relate to the various consonants, for the following meanings?

Fl – meaning lightness and grace
Sp – for forceful, outward movement
Fl – meaning ungainly, awkward movement
Cr – meaning unpleasant sounds
St – meaning lack of movement
Gl – meaning light
L – meaning depraved or highly-sexed
Wh – meaning rush of air or breath
Sw – meaning graceful motion
Sw – meaning more violent motion
Obs – meaning unpleasant
Gr – meaning out of sorts, harsh or unpleasant
Qu – meaning unpleasant connotations
Sl – meaning mire
Y – meaning sounds
Wh – meaning sounds
Sh – meaning reduction in size

If, without consulting a dictionary, you can get five in each of the above categories, you are sensational. The general grading is:

Excellent   5 in each category minimum
Good   3 in each category
Fair   1 in each category

If you should go wild in any one category, add one point. If you should find words which are not listed in the reading part of the chapter, add one point for each word.

chapter five

MORE FUN WITH WORDS—
DIVISION OF FRACTURED GEOGRAPHY

Note to Game Maniacs:

The usual games based on this literary material
are at the back of the chapter, on page 55. You
may want to try them out first before you savor
the metaphysical impact of the reading material
of the chapter, where most of the answers are
lurking, if indeed there are answers.

JUSTA, MINN.   NEV, VA.!

Psychiatry continues to gain in popularity. In fact, I once knew of a psychiatrist who was so popular that the world beat a psychopath to his door. But nothing could be as whacky as the response to a little item I once ran in *Trade Winds* in an unsuspecting moment. The item ran:

"Kate Rodina Steichen has been hard at work on a new geographical twister that may well drive cartographers to heavy drink. She has succeeded in creating unlikely towns for all but eighteen states in the Union, in the following fashion: Noah's, Ark.; Ex, Conn.; Outsidemy, Ken.; Near, Miss.; Hoot, Mon.; Either, Ore.; Ballpoint, Penn.; Fiveand, Tenn. If you care to develop this further, we commend you, as Shakespeare would say, to your own content."

The response from readers brought loud complaints from my postman, who failed to see the humor of the situation. And while space will not permit (as the rocket designer said to the astronaut) a full analysis, a quick rundown of the overall response brings out these facts:

Twelve respondents submitted No, Cal.; nine, Metre, Cal. Nearly every respondent included a tribute to Illinois, nearly all of them with the same meaning in different ways: Gravely, Ill.; Feeling, Ill.; Never, Ill.; U-look, Ill.; Slightly, Ill.; Sorta, Ill.; Very, Ill.; Reeley, Ill.

Hoop, La. was a popular favorite, as well as Requiem, Mass.; Ding Dong, Del.; Vita, Minn.; and Dunno, Alaska.

Russell Miles, of the University of Illinois, came through with four biographical towns, such as: Guinan, Tex.; Coolidge, Cal.; Miller, Mich.; and Williams, Tenn.

The Conklins of Bon Air, Virginia, suggested a blockbusting twister with Honisoiquimaly, Pa.; while John Stevens offered Income, Tex. But the first unofficial, nonredeemable, and no-cash award went to Margaret Bennett of Sherman Oaks, California, who came up with the town of Nohitsno-runsno, Ariz.

Second prize went to Marie Longyear and Delight Ansley of McGraw-Hill for Seething, Mass. and Faux, Pa.

Kate Steichen's original attempt to cover all the states of the Union may have failed in reaching its goal, but the attempt is worthy:

Thewillof, Ala.	Inthe, Maine
Wait, Alaska	Ohdear, Me.
Noah's, Ark.	Early, Mass.
No, Cal.	Near, Miss.
Salaam, Calif.	No, Mo.
Ex, Conn.	Hoot, Mon.
Thefarmerinthe, Del.	Either, Ore.
Ga, Ga.	Idoodit, Pa.
Imfine, Hawaii	Ballpoint, Penn.
Ifheda, Ida.	Fiveand, Tenn.
Feelin, Ill.	Yoohoo, Virginia
Athou, Iowa	Elle, Va.
Ithinki, Kan.	Itwont, Wash.
Outsidemy, Ken.	Heeza, Wis.
Oola, La.	Wyowyo, Wyo.

And, as if that wasn't enough, her friends and family rallied to her aid for supporting lists of this hideously fractured geography:

Daddy, O.; Pigg, Penn.; Garbage, Kan.; Kiss, Me.; La, La.; Yes, Pa. (Mary Steichen Calderone)

Iaintgrammatical, R. I.; Deathan, Texas; Bowsn, Ariz.; Taketea, N. C. (Joanna Taub Steichen)

Praise, Ala.; Tight, Colo.; Proand, Conn.; Infi, Del.; Sussk, Ind.; Allihave, Iowa; Junior, Miss.; Syno, N. M.; Laymedoon, N. D. (Carol Silverberg)

Other lists were equally atrocious:

From Richard Wands: Cockney's Drop, N. H.; Boystood-onaburn, N. D.; Proer, Conn.; Dead, Alas.; Half Pass, Tenn.; Greengrowthelilacs, O.; Thisisthe, Ind.

From Kenneth R. Mitchell: G. Thirza Mighty Pretty, Miss.; Critical, Mass.

From Mrs. Wilbert White: PeptoBis, Mo.; Ben Casey, Md.; Kentucky, Col.; Whis, Ky.; Justa, Minn.

Schools seemed to respond in a yeoman fashion to the Steichen folly. Miss Jill Zemans, age 12, sent us a list made up by her sixth grade class, which included, in part: Tra la, La.; Apple, P. I.*; Tin, Kans.; Ron, Del.; Infi, Del.; Eski, Mo.; Drink, R. I.; Rainbow, Ark.; Hitand, Miss.

And Karl Decker writes: "I teach English, 10th grade, and stuck a half a dozen of the fractured geography phrases on the board this dreary Friday morning. Came back at 2:30. Two or three classes had gone through the room that day. Board completely covered with the following:"

Water, Maine	Greatvig, Ga.
Iron, Ore.	Et, Al.
Hog, Wash.	Scotchand, R. I.
Play, Tex.	Drain, O.
Thumb, Tex.	Nev, Va.
New Pink, Wisc.	Hind, Ind.
Doremefaso, La.	Wih, Minn.

* Miss Zemans has decided to annex the Philippines.

Aardv, Ark.	Faux, Pa.
Pro, Miss.	Bro, Mo.
Aly, Kan.	Thereisnothinglikeaday, Me.
Oz, Ark.	Eggsandbay, Conn.

Not satisfied with geography alone, E. S. Colling sat down at his desk in Yarnell, Arizona, and created a few people to go along with the fractured villages:

A. Voir Dupois	Lotta Kirves
Metre, Cal.	Oola, La.
S. O. Wye	Daily Food
Cantey, Wyo.	Supple, Mont.
4–A	A. Swee
Whiter, Wash.	Tasapples, Ida.
Justin Faire	
Arbitrate, Ore.	

Another variation of such fractured geography sprang up from under a rock, the idea of which is to pick a town or city and give it a definition of a highly unlikely sort. For instance, what town in Pennsylvania gives you a ghostly feeling? And the answer, as if you hadn't already guessed, is Erie.

Others include:

In what town in Texas is a girl never safe?
Answer: El Paso.

What county in Massachusetts is entirely neuter?
Answer: Middlesex.

What town in Indiana creates all the modern popular dances?
Answer: South Bend.

What city in Michigan specializes in surgery?
Answer: Lansing.

What city in Kansas is full of Peeping Toms?
Answer: Topeka.

You're entirely on your own if you want to continue this frightful game.

Wherever you go, you're likely to find geography, and with these games haunting you, you'll forever be losing sleep. One particular thing about geography, however, keeps haunting me. It's an item Dan Blumenthal sent me from a travel piece in *Cue* magazine:

"In the Caribbean, Puerto Rico offers limitless possibilities . . . and the U. S. Virgins are prepared for you, with hundreds of new hotel rooms."

GAMES FOR CHAPTER FIVE

Fractured Geography, Virginia, is not a game. It is a way of life. Just how you play it is for the most part up to you. However, you might first start in this way:

(1) Find one excrutiatingly bad double-meaning town for each state in the Union. Example: Dunno, Alaska; Gravely, Ill.

(2) Score yourself 1 point for each state you are able to cover.

(3) Grade yourself, or your guests:

Excellent	40
Good	30
Fair	20

Another variation is to take the following list, and to see if you can find states, or their abbreviations, to go with the following towns:

Thewillof, ——	Oola, ——
Wait, ——	Inthe, ——
Noah's, ——	Ohdear, ——
Ex, ——	Requiem, ——
Thefarmerinthe, ——	Near, ——
Imfine, ——	Hoot, ——
Ifheda, ——	Either, ——
Feelin, ——	Idoodit, ——
Ithinki, ——	Proand, ——
Outsidemy, ——	Infi, ——

Ballpoint, ——	Praise, ——
Fiveand, ——	Tight, ——
Itwont, ——	Allihave, ——
Heeza, ——	Laymedoon, ——
Whyowhyo, ——	Cockney's Drop, ——
Garbage, ——	Greengrowthelilacs, ——
Kiss, ——	Faux, ——
Deathan, ——	Eggsandbay, ——

Score yourself, if you're still alive, on the following basis:

Excellent	30
Good	20
Fair	10

(Note: There is some doubt that if you score high in any of these games that you are to be congratulated. It may mean only that you have a severe deficiency of some kind. So those who score low may take heart at any time, and are free to talk about the high scorers in muffled tones, behind their backs.)

Fractured Geography II is a game for those who are not already surfeited with the above.

Its concept is simple: Take any town or city and find a double-meaning definition for it. Example: What city in Pennsylvania gives you a ghostly feeling? Answer: Erie.

Grade yourself:

Excellent	5 towns and definitions
Good	3 towns and definitions
Fair	2 towns and definitions

chapter six

STILL MORE QUESTIONABLE FUN WITH WORDS

Note to Game Maniacs:

By now you may have become emotionally exhausted, and will welcome the sprightly reading portion of the chapter. If you do, you'll be sadly disappointed, because there are so many games we have to cram in here, there is practically no reading portion to the chapter. So you may as well turn to page 80, and try your hand at the games first.

There is a famous old classic sentence, long used by English teachers as a stiff test of a student's ability to punctuate:

John where Jim had had had had had had had.

As most of you recall, the corrected punctuated version comes out:

John, where Jim had had "had," had had "had had."

This sleeping dog had been lying still a long time, until Clyde Carter, from University City, Missouri, opened up a whole new can of rhetoric by asking: What would happen if *another* John and Jim were given the sentence to punctuate, and John had given up in disgust?

He figures the situation would then come out something like this:

John, where Jim had had "John, where Jim had had 'had,' had had 'had had,'" had had "John where Jim had had had had had had had."

"This brings me to the absolutely unpleasant thought," Mr.

Carter's letter goes on, "that *still another* John and Jim might get involved to produce almost impossible complications."

Within days, more mail came in to add to the confusion. Albert Ewell, Chairman of the Department of Psychology at Middlebury College recalled that the original sentence was still more complex:

John where Jim had had had had had had had had had had had had had a better effect on the teacher than had had had.

Not content to let sleeping hads lie, Mildred Finck and her high school son immediately put their heads together to come out with this concoction:

Had Jim had had "John, where Jim had had 'John, where Jim had had 'had' had had that "That 'that' that that man said should have been 'this'"" had had 'John, where Jim had had 'had' had had that "That 'that' that that man said should have been 'which,'"" we'd all have been had."

Mrs. Finck concludes her note: "I'm sure there are further refinements to this torture, but right now I'm not up to it."

Of course, if anyone is exhausted by all this, all he needs to do is turn to the next one:

> that that is is that that is not is not
> is that that it is . . .

As an out to all this, you can always turn to what Harriet Kopelman calls *Spicy Proverbs*. She has put together a list which includes:

A tarragon of virtue
A fool anise money are soon parted
Thyme is of the essence
Seeing is bay-leaving

Or as Marcia Ringel adds, a woman went to the store to get some herbs, and came back empty handed. Explaining the situation, she said: "The joint is out of thyme."

Ed Horr, however, likes his proverbs to be of a more theological nature. His letter tells about a church which was considering adding an assistant minister to their overloaded preacher. But the elders turned down the idea with the statement: "One wise to the Word is sufficient."

Ever since Garson Kanin created the character of Billie Dawn in *Born Yesterday*, the word *couth* has come into popularity in the language, meaning the opposite of its parent word *uncouth*. (Actually, there is an obsolete legitimate word *couth*, meaning *known, familiar* or *noted*.)

Other derivatives of Billie Dawn's malapropisms include:

> *Ept,* meaning skilful and full of aptitude
> *Augurated,* meaning a president kicked out of office
> *Anthrope,* a fellow who loves his fellow men

Delight Ansley, of New York City, would add a few of her own:

> *Cognito:* well-known
> *Maculate:* dirty
> *Mantle:* to set up
> *Trepid:* cowardly
> *Plussed:* confident

Bob Blumenthal and Phil Shopoff have put their prefixes together to come up with their own list:

> Something that's in the middle is on the TERIOR
> When you add something to something, you LETE
> When you start something the first time, you SUME
> When you discuss something for the first time, you HASH
> When you dislike something for the first time, you are PULSED by it
> Something you like is GUSTING
> When you say something for the first time, you PEAT

When you think of something the first time, you MEM-
   BER it

The outstanding members of society are GENERATES

That which turns around the first time VOLVES

Acquired knowledge is STINCTIVE

Acceptable forms of intra-family relations are defined as
   CEST

An appreciative person is a GRATE

When you originally sign up for something, you
   GISTER

The materials which must be brought into a country are
   DIGENOUS to that country.

David McCord, in turn, has a delightful verse on truncated
words of the Spare-the-Prefix category:

I now a little man both ept and ert
An intro? extro? No, he's just a vert
Sheveled and couth and kept, pecunious, ane:
His image trudes upon the ceptive brain.

Of course a lot of spare-the-prefix words come naturally.
Like Oscar Shefler's two-year-old son who was scolded at dinner. The father turned to the boy sharply and said: "Michael,
behave!"

The son looked at the father blankly and said: "Father are
you being 'have?"

It was Dr. Lester Ford who brought to my attention a word
game which he believes was originated by Lewis Carroll. The
problem is to find words that will include such unlikely combinations of letters as XYG, TOMO, HEON, etc. (The answers for these are oXYGen, auTOMObile, luncHEON.)
Others on Dr. Ford's list include:

XOP	saxophone
DHP	jodhpurs
RIJU	marijuana

OMAHA   tomahawk
ZOP   schizophrenia

Although we don't recommend you send any of these by telegram, unless you want to be suspected as an international spy, here are a few more to mull over:

AGAMU   ragamuffin
RYG   drygoods
ERGRO   underground
HTH   eighth
RND   dirndl
YZY   syzygy
MIKA   mikado, kamikaze

Not content with ordinary word-twisters, Walter Leight, of San Diego, sent along these problems:

Find words which
(1) contain four successive letters of the alphabet, in alphabetical sequence
(2) contain five consecutive vowels, preferably different
(3) contain five or more consecutive consonants
(4) contain double letters, one word for each letter of the alphabet

For the record, we list Mr. Leight's fiendish chicanery:

(1) gyMNOPlast, undeRSTUdy
(2) mIAOUEd
(3) boRSCHT
(4) Excluding the obvious doubles:
krAAl   zaQQum
witHHold   chiVVy
skIIng   poWWow
haJJi   saYYid
chuKKer

As far as XX goes, you have to cheat a little and use something like Jimmy FoXX, the former baseball great, who also features a double *M* in his first name.

Palindromes have had a long play, ever since the famous quote about Napoleon: "Able was I ere I saw Elba." This reads the same way forward and backward, and the search has been going on for years for equally apt phrases.

"Madam, I'm Adam" is of course another classic. And in Detroit, Gordon Jett has been making a long list of palindromes for his own amusement. "The whole thing started for me," he writes, "when I went to work for a man named: Otto Renner."

In Hollywood, Jason Lindsey has compiled his own list of palindrome words such as ere, bib, did, bob, dud, eke, ewe, eye, kayak, level, refer, radar, reviver, rotator, deified, and so forth. But no professional would be content with this sort of child's play. His search now is for words, which, when spelled backwards, form *another* word:

straw	warts
diaper	repaid
stinker	reknits
deliver	reviled
dessert	tressed

These are just a few of his staggering list of *semordnilap*—which, of course, is palindromes spelled backwards.

You might, if you're of a mind to do it, join in with Dorothy Beers in her search for words which sound the same, but still have different meanings. Her first selection consists of *raise* and *raze*, and I've received a swarm of letters pointing out that *cleave* (to adhere) and *cleave* (to divide) make ideal candidates for the club.

Other word-spotters have come up with things like:

From James R. C. Adams:

Seed	(seed the lawn)
Seed	(de-pit the cherries)

From Eleanor Chapman:

Wholly	(complete or entire)
Holey	(incomplete, not entire)
Secrete	(to hide)
Secrete	(to extrude, to give forth)

From Joseph Caro:

Peer	(an equal in standing or rank)
Peer	(nobility, of higher rank)
Unit	(a complete thing, an undivided entity)
Unit	(a part of a complete thing)
Let	(a verb, meaning to permit or allow)
Let	(a noun, which means an obstruction or hindrance)
Scan	(to read hastily)
Scan	(to examine carefully)
Hold	(to hold a meeting now)
Hold	(to postpone)
Blunt	(a blunt person makes sharp or pointed remarks)
Blunt	(not sharp, without an edge)
Fast	(rapid in motion)
Fast	(remaining motionless—boat fast to pier)

Ida Selavan has another startling idea. She points out that a MATERNITY DRESS might lead to a PATERNITY SUIT—and the meanings are quite different.

And then Mrs. H. Patcher starts a whole new ball rolling by suggesting this: How about "invaluable" being more valuable than "valuable"; and "shameless" being more shameful than "shameful"?

Is there no end to this sort of thing?

Putting the horse before the cart has led to all sorts of trouble, but none worse than the flood of gags arising from putting the answer before the questions. One of the most famous is:

Answer: 9-W
Question: Herr Wagner, do you spell your name with a V?

Steve Allen has put dozens of these together in his amusing book *The Question Man,* which you'll enjoy reading any time of night or day. But another amusement you might put your mind to is to take the names of companies in whatever area your career is, and create your own question-man format. I tried it out in the publishing business, with these results:

Answer: Harper's
Question: Who plays them big gold things with strings?

Answer: Duell, Sloan, and Pearce.
Question: What did they tell Sloan when he took fencing lessons?

Answer: Doubleday.
Question: What wages do they pay you when you work on Sundays and holidays?

Answer: Indiana University Press.
Question: What did the cheering section yell out in Indiana?

Answer: Little, Brown
Question: How would you describe a midget sun-bather?

Answer: Dodd, Mead.
Question: Wha' dod stuff Beowulf got drunk on?

Answer: Putnam.

Question: Ike, what are you doing now that you're no longer president?

Just when I had started on a campaign to prevent habit-forming games or gamelets from getting a toehold, James Alemany came along with a new agonizer he called *Chaucer.* The examples will give you an idea:

Mark Twain wrote a book about what his hero would do after his best friend died. (Huck'll Bury Finn)

Sir Walter Scott wrote about what the Russian farmer does. (Ivan hoe)

J. D. Salinger wrote about what the husband would do if he came home and found his wife in a tub full of whisky. (Catch Her in the Rye)

The all-time best seller tells us what the cow said as her favorite gentleman friend was leaving the pasture. (Bye, Bull)

Bizet wrote an opera about garage mechanics. (Car Men)

Just to make matters incurably worse, Mr. Alemany concludes with the title of a magazine for an oversexed milk farm:

Satyr Dairy View.

Spurred on by such nonsense, Carol Whitcraft has come up with:

What Chubby Checkers said about a cute young London dancer. (Ah Love 'er twist)

Herman Wouk remarking on the bereavement of a madam. (Ma Jorie mourns Ingstar)

A girl from the Shining Big Sea Water says to a home-town writer. (Hya Autha)

Marjorie Wihtol also responds admirably:

A book on mixed drinks. (Oliver Twist)

A history of window-cleaners. (Generation of Wipers)

Reminiscences of an English gardener. (I've an Hoe)

Book by an East German baker. (The Scarlet Pumpernickel)

A graceful way to get out of all this is to record Joe Tockman's comment on the remarks of a college lit class: Hawthorne's Hester Prynne was not entitled to an A. A *C-plus* would have been a more deserving grade.

Or you might be interested in the conversation which Malcom Ferguson unreliably reports.

The late Leopold von Sacher-Masoch: "By the way, mon vieux, I'm writing a book entitled *It Only Hurts When I Smile*."

The late Marquis de Sade: "Remarkable. My book is to be called *I Only Smile When It Hurts*."

The late, great Colonel Stoopnagle was unmatched when it came to definitions, or daffynitions, as he called them. One of his classics was a *mano-kleptiac*: A person who goes around putting stolen goods back on department store counters. Another was his definition of a door knob: Something that a revolving door goes around without.

Now Jack Gordon of New York has come along with a new game he'd like to make people suffer with called Definition. For a start, he suggests:

Ramshackle: A chain used to tie up a he-goat.

If all the game ideas of people were laid end to end, the chances are you'd trip over them. In brief form, we'll try to cover some more of them, taking no responsibility for the red-rimmed eyes that some of them might cause:

Cliché Dropping is the twisted brain child of J. Tyler Dunn and Audrey Carroll. Object: Combine favorite clichés with the names of celebrated people.

CLOTHES MAKE THE Jayne MANsfield.
KEEP A STIFF UPPER Walter LIPpman.
IT'S NOT THE Gabriel HEATer, IT'S THE HUMIDI T. S. Eliot.
IF THE Willie SHOEmaker F. Scott FITZgerald, PUT IT ON.
Lord HOME IS WHERE THE William S. HART IS.
An Elaine STRITCH IN TIME SAVES Ernest Borg-NINE.
EAST IS Max EASTman AND WEST IS Paul WESTon, AND NEVER THE John ColTRANE SHALL Vaughan MEADer.

Conversation Piece is an inexcusable game perpetrated by Colin Sanderson. Object: Take a subject, any subject, and mangle it like this:

Girl: Orangejuice sorry you made me cry?
Boy: Don't be soda pressed; them martini bruises.
Girl: Wine you leave me alone?
Boy: Water you mean? I didn't even have to let gin.
Girl: Oh, why Chianti leave me alone?
Boy: Look, vodkan I do to make it all rye?
Girl: Just leave me beer I'll scream.
Boy: Oh, I'd like tequila.
Girl: Darling, let's give up bourbon life. There's more rum in the country.

Retouch is a game Paul Kirkpatrick would like to get off the ground. He's looking for words which require a lot of re-touching, where you have to go back as many times as possible to dot the i's and cross the t's.

Two qualifying champions to date: *extraterritoriality* and *internationalization*.

Each of these words require seven "retouching" jobs.

Exclamation—Without Point comes from Jerre Mangione, a game he used to practice as a youth. It involves a series of this sort:

What, no mummy?
Tut, tut!

What, no drama?
Pshaw!

What, no corn?
Shucks!

"These examples," Mr. Mangione writes, "may explain my reluctance to take any credit for inventing the game—if indeed I ever did."

Marvin Preiser doesn't waste any time in adding: What, torn socks? Darn! And Larry Brilliant notes that comic books offer a convenient source of inspirational exclamational material:

What, no puppy?
Dog-gone!

What, no Brutus?
Great Caesar's Ghost!

What, no vowels?
Oh!

What, no Boulder?
Damn!

What, no silence?
Zounds!

Duple puns have R. S. Peterson working overtime, although he claims: "Duple puns I can get them for you wholesale.

What I want for my collection is more tripple-tonguing tipple punning." His efforts are yeoman:

would not
wood knot

know you would not
no yew wood knot

I know you would not
Aye, no yew wood knot

Famous Passes helps while away the time for Bob Busby, when he's not busy at the City Desk of the Kansas City *Star*. They include:

Thou shalt not . . .
Pippa . . .
Kybher . . .
Faux . . .
Ships that . . .
. . . at girls who wear glasses.

Classic Cognometry has fascinated Bob Peck and Phil Desmond. They would develop such enterprises as:

Habeas and Corpus, Undertakers
Ipso Facto, Inc., data processors
Lux et Veritas, honest electricians
Ave atque Vale Tours, Inc.
De Profundis, Inc., Well diggers
Caveat Emptor, Inc., Used Cars

Redundancy Hunting is the indoor sport of Howard P. Hudson. He heard a sports broadcaster, for instance, describe Patty Berg as a "leading female woman golfer." In the same interview, Miss Berg continued: "I'm going to Europe, and then I'm going to the Continent."

Unlikely Double Features is a standby of Harriet Silverman. She would book films like the following into the Neighborhood houses:

THE KEY
THE APARTMENT

IF A MAN ANSWERS
SORRY, WRONG NUMBER

GIANT
THE INCREDIBLE SHRINKING MAN

SAYONARA
HELLO, DOLLY

Political Queens are of interest to Lyman Parrigin, III. He suggests that in place of Miss America, we elect the following:

NATO (Miss Alliance)
Senate Finance Committee (Miss Appropriate)
CIA (Miss Informed)
U.N. translator (Miss Interpretation)

Payola comes from Burt Kaufman, of Boston, inspired by the radio and television scandals of yesteryear. He would suggest:

For crayon companies sending out samples (Crayola)
TV writers getting a discount on a set (Motorola)
Bootblack accepting a sample can of polish (Shinola)
For disc jockeys, who started the whole thing (Victrola)

Four Word Wisdom is a hobby of Sam Marx, the Hollywood producer, and he has discovered that a lot of wisdom can be packed into that many words. The moral may be: If you can't say it in four words, don't say it:

In God we trust
This, too, shall pass

Live and let live
Still waters run deep
Bad news travels fast
Love laughs at locksmiths
Nothing succeeds like success
Charity begins at home
Politics makes strange bedfellows
Nothing ventured, nothing gained
Man proposes, God disposes
Let sleeping dogs lie

But Athene Fekas adds that if you can't say it in four words, you might as well say it in one: *Perastika*, in Greek, means "This too shall pass."

Cross Breed is a game created by Ralph Cokain, in which you cross a few unlikely categories and come up with something entirely new:

Cross a British nobleman with a suitmaker, and you come up with: Lord & Taylor.
Cross the Pentagon with United Parcel: General Delivery.
Cross a slide fastener with a telegraph operator: Zip code.

Meaningless Nothings is the game from the authors Kelley Roos (Audrey and William Roos, who write mysteries under that name), whose thriller from Dodd, Mead, *Necessary Evil*, aroused so much attention. The trick of their game is to find as many nonsense phrases as possible on this basis:

A chainless end
A pitless bottom
A gameless score
A bra-less strap
A gemless flaw
A jobless thank
A hatless brim

A stockingless seam
A caseless hope
A deathless pain
A rumorless base
A searchless fruit
A tail-less end

A *Twisted Olympics* is the suggestion of M. Lloyd Bond. This would include: Windmill Tilting, Conclusion Jumping, Fulltilt Running, Foot Dragging, Infinitive Splitting, and so forth. The Bond family claims to have lined up 750 of such events.

Alphabetic Sentences, without strict Olympic rules, is a new game conjured up by John Moffatt and Don Carns. Example: "Abelard, Being Confused, Denounced Excessive Folly, Grew Heated In Justifying Knowledge, Loving Music, Not Other People, Quite Renouncing Sexual Temptation, Undertook Variously Woodwinds, Xylophones, Yodeling, Zithers."

Adventures in Alliterature is a game springing from Churchill Satterlee's fevered brain. He likes to compile cohesive groups of alliterate words, confining his culling to two consecutive pages of the dictionary being used. Example:
"While spurring some spunk with a spudder, the spurrier, with a sprunt, spurtled a spruit of spunkie on the spurge and spurry." (*Webster's New International*, Second Edition, pages 2443 and 2444.) Translation: "While gashing some touchwood with a tool for removing bark from timber, the spur-maker, with a start, spit out a stream of hard liquor on the shrubs and weeds."

Transitional Logic and the Atrocious Pun is the label attached to this horrifying game of Harry Kuris's. He would, for instance, set out to prove, of all things, that a sheet of paper is a lazy dog:

(1) A sheet of paper is an ink-lined plane
(2) An inclined plane is a slope up
(3) A slow pup is a lazy dog

Rhyming What-Is-Its might be the title for the game of William Kite, of Bala-Cynwyd, Pa. He asks if anyone can think of another pair of relatively unfamiliar words, that could be substituted in this verse:

A thorp
Is a dorp.

And believe it or not, a thorp *is* a dorp. Look it up.

Substitution (Foreign Words Division) is a game which SFC would foist upon an unsuspecting public. He discovered that "bernstein" means "amber" in German. "I feel," he writes, "that Kathleen Winsor would have gotten nowhere if she had written a book titled *Forever Bernstein*—and there must be a lot of other titles this switch would work on."

That's the Way the Cookie Crumbles is the personal game of Joy Daniels, and her research has developed a whole new series for this expression of the modern day. Examples:

That's the way the bed spreads
. . . the meat loafs
. . . the kitchen sinks
. . . the ivory coasts
. . . the star fishes
. . . the pillow fights
. . . the autumn leaves
. . . the coffee grinds

Miss Daniels claims that she got up to 750 of these.

Happy Birthday is a game from Mark Koppel and his room-mates Messrs. Butler and Helterman. The names to which he would send greetings are:

Kay Sirrah (Italian)
Jay Fam (French)
Mary Ann Haste
Judy Obscure
Bella de Ball

College Catalog comes from Gibson Reaves, who would find appropriate adjectives to describe the work of his colleagues. The lectures of each of the following may be described:

Professor of Music	Noteworthy
Professor of Oceanography	Unfathomable
Professor of Transportation	Moving
Professor of Religion	Divine
Professor of Speech Therapy	Unspeakable
Professor of Botany	Pithy
Professor of Marriage Counseling	Well-conceived
Professor of Architecture	Edifying

Next Letter comes from the pen of Kermet Parker. He calls it an extension of the old Victor Borge game (Reminder: Won-derful becomes two-derful). Mr. Parker goes wilder. He would substitute the sound of the next letter of the alphabet, so that "heart" would be "hest." Examples:

"Ceelpea thef nefs ess oakems."
(Translation: Below the knees are ankles.)

"Vee ess be aitchraffe, he's beep veemess, jay'm oh peeled zeese emgeecat."
(Translation: You are a giraffe, he's a puma, I'm a wise, old elephant.)

Malaproposits is the name given by Ethel Wollman to her game for insomniacs. Examples: To expose is to quit modeling. Olfactory is an elderly mill that smells. An intent is an at-home when you are on a camping trip. A mandate is a rendezvous with a fella. A porthole is the open end of a wine bottle.

Match-pub is the game from John O'Connor, of Philadelphia, who would suggest that you take the following list of titles, and match them to the most appropriate publishers below. The books: (1) Techniques of Public Opinion Polling (2) A Kiss in Bed (3) The Art of Diplomacy (4) A History of the Polo Grounds (5) Mal de Mer in the Harbor (6) Time Organization—the Key to Success.

The publishers to match up with the above: (1) Random House (2) Lippincott (3) Wiley (4) McGraw-Hill (5) Basic (6) Doubleday.

By the same token, Mrs. John Foley of Joliet, Illinois, ascribes several books to appropriate publishers. Among them are *The Stan Musial Story* (Cardinal Editions) and *Confessions of a Purse Snatcher* (Pocket Books).

Color It Color is still *another* variation of the Victor Borge syndrome, coming from Pauline Engel. Instead of changing numbers in word syllables, she would change colors. Thus, a-blu-tions becomes a-brown-tions. So, when you're ready to go, you're blue-y; a tangerine turns into a green-gerine, and it all turns out that Tom Sawyer purple-washed his fence and ate beigeberry pie.

Pluralities has been an old, hoary game since the beginning of time (Example: A giggle of teen agers, a pad of beatniks), but a fresh slant has come from London medical circles, as Lily Bock writes regarding a clipping in the *Journal of the AMA*. The new batch includes:

A rash of dermatologists
A hive of allergists
A scrub of internes
A flood of urologists
An eyeful of ophthamologists
A staph of bacteriologists
A gargle of laryngologists

Half Noun-Half Verb is the brainchild of F. K. Plous, Jr., and Victor Lukas, in which they search for words where the first half of a noun is a verb, and the second half is that same verb's direct object. Examples:

breakfast
carryall
cutthroat
killjoy
passport
scapegrace
scofflaw
turncoat

"Nowadays," they write, "such terms seem to get turned around, with the object preceding and the verb following, and an -er tacked on to the end—such as 'penny-pincher.' And not only did Shakespeare use such terms, but his own surname falls into the same category."

Up and Down is another game from the ubiquitous pen of Dorothy Beers. She manages to while away the hours until dawn by trying to find two words or expressions, one containing the word "up" and the other "down." Examples:

Shut up	Pipe down
Upbraid	Dress down
Catch up with	Track down
Downcast	Upset

Take up residence	Settle down
Close down	Fold up
Lay down your arms	Deliver up your arms
Lay down your life	Give up the ghost
Turn your nose up at	Look down your nose at

While we're on the subject of words, it's interesting to note that Lincoln Barnet catapults some telling slings and arrows at those who are hell-bent on degrading the English language by embracing the "free-write" school of authorship.

Among his targets is novelist William Burroughs, who has neither the erudition nor the poetic genius of James Joyce, as Barnet points out, but who seems to work overtime to achieve unintelligibility. In his crusade to muddle and confuse the reader, Burroughs has developed what he calls the "fold-in" method of writing. Burroughs confesses that he might take page one of his manuscript, and fold it down the middle. He does the same with page 100, then matches them up to form a composite page. The resulting collage is supposed to result in great art.

Mr. Barnet takes as dim a view as I do of this sort of acrobatic pagination, but just to prove that I'm open-minded about the whole situation, I took a recent letter of complaint I wrote to a typewriter company, and folded it in with one of Hamlet's soliloquies. The result follows:

Now I am alone. Oh, what a rogue and
complaint about my electric typewriter,
not monstrous that this player here,
the dealer for the fourth time
with passion should force his soul so
to sounding like an anvil chorus
her working all her visage waned. Tears
on it seem to me that if you
in his aspect, and his whole shape suiting
which sells considerably above the price of peanuts

and all for nothing. For Hecuba. What's
to the interest of your company to
motive and cue for passion that I have
considering the entire machine with
tears, and cleave the general ear
up to parts drop off.
Make mad the guilty and appal the free.
And even my secretary finds it hard to
peek like John-a-dreams,
continually borders on the outskirts of
do nothing, no, not for a king upon whose property
that this letter is in handwriting.
That I am pigeon-livered and lack gall
malfunction every time I hit the damn space bar.
Or ere this I should have fatted
serious attention to shoring up
bloody, bawdy villain.
At the next model you bring out,
will be most brave, that I the son of a dear
letters of complaint . . .

On second thought, maybe Burroughs is right. It just
might sell in today's market.

GAMES FOR CHAPTER SIX

GRAMMARVILLE SPECIAL

Take the famous old punctuation test sentence:

John where Jim had had had had had had had.

Then:

(1) See if you remember how to punctuate it.

(2) Take two aspirin or one tranquillizer, and then try to figure this out: What if *another* John and Jim were given the same sentence to punctuate? How would the sentence read?

(3) Taking the situation immediately above in (2), suppose Jim had had this sentence in place of the original:

"that that is is that that is not is not is not that it it is"

(4) First see if you can remember how you used to punctuate that old turkey, and then work it into the composite sentence as in (2).

(5) Phone your doctor immediately if pain persists.

SPICY PROVERBS

Take the names of famous spices, and complete these sentences:

(1) A —— of virtue
(2) A fool —— money are soon parted
(3) —— is of the essence
(4) Seeing is ——ing.

Excellent	3
Good	2
Fair	1

Add 3 points for every original you can make up.

SPARE THE PREFIX

Remove the prefix from certain words, and make up your own list of truncated words with new meanings. You may, if you wish, try your hand at this list first. (Example: *couth*—meaning well-groomed)

_____ skilful and full of aptitude
_____ president kicked out of office
_____ a fellow who loves his fellow men
_____ well-known
_____ dirty
_____ to set up
_____ cowardly
_____ confident, not confused

Excellent	8
Good	6
Fair	4

See if you can get a reasonable, if any, definition for each of the following truncated words. (Example; when you start something for the first time, you SUME)

TERIOR	GENERATES
LETE	VOLVES
HASH	STINCTIVE
PULSED	CEST
GUSTING	GRATE
PEAT	GISTER
MEMBER	DIGENOUS

Excellent	10
Good	8
Fair	6

THE GAME OF SHRDLU

Find words which will include these unlikely combinations of letters: (Example: XOP – saxophone)

DHP	ERGRO
RIJU	HTH
OMAHA	RND
ZOP	YZY
AGAMU	MIKA
RYG	

Excellent	6
Good	4
Fair	2

No one is going to twist your arm to complete this portion of the game. However, if you must, try to find the following:

(1) Find words which contain four successive letters of the alphabet, in alphabetical sequence.

(2) Contain five consecutive vowels, preferably different.

(3) Contain five or more consecutive consonants.

(4) Contain double letters, one word for each letter of the alphabet.

NO SCORE ON THIS; IF YOU GET ANY, YOU DE-SERVE A MEDAL

OLD FASHIONED PALINDROMES

Find words which read the same way forward and backward for the following:

k---k
l---l
r---r
r---r
r-----r
r-----r
d-----d

Excellent 5
Good   4
Fair   3

In the following list, take the definition, find the word for it in which the discovered word makes another word spelled backward. (Example: Straw—Warts)

(1) Mother's lament
(2) A rat fink
(3) What an obstetrician does
(4) Not for a calorie counter

Excellent 3
Good   2
Fair   1

THE SAME DIFFERENCE

Find as many words as you can which are spelled or pronounced the same, but which have opposite meanings. (Example: Cleave, to adhere; cleave, to divide)

Excellent 5
Good   3
Fair   2

CHAUCER

See if you can find the book which the following definitions represent. (Example: Sir Walter Scott wrote about what a Russian farmer does: Ivan hoe.)

Mark Twain wrote a book about what his hero would do after his best friend died. (————)

J. D. Salinger wrote a book about what the husband would do if he came home and found his wife in a tub full of whisky. (————)

An all time best seller tells us what the cow said as her favorite gentleman friend was leaving the pasture. (————)

Bizet wrote an opera about garage mechanics. (————)

A book on how you might want a mixed drink. (————)

Since you should have no trouble at all with this one, there are regretfully no points awarded.

THE FOLLOWING ARE BARELY GAMES, BUT THERE ARE ENOUGH BRAIN-TWISTER STOPPERS AMONG THEM TO CONTRIBUTE TO A GRADUAL LOSS OF SANITY. SCORING IS ON AN HONOR SYSTEM: AFTER YOU'VE TRIED THEM, DETERMINE YOUR OWN SCORE ON THE BASIS OF HOW YOU FEEL AFTERWARD. AND, AS THEY SAY IN HOLLYWOOD, LET NO MAN RE-WRITE YOUR EPITAPH.

(1) Find two words where you have to go back and cross the "t" and dot the "i" for a total of seven times in each word.

(2) How many more of these can you put together? Example: "What—no Mummy? Tut, tut."

(3) The following have identical punning words which make sense. Can you figure them out:

would not

know you would not

I know you would not

(4) How many "famous passes" can you list, like: Pippa ———. Faux ———.

(5) How many unlikely "double features" can you list which would startle moviegoers on the marquee? Example: THE KEY, and THE APARTMENT.

(6) In place of Miss America, how many other beauty queens can you list like the following: Miss Alliance, selected by NATO.

(7) Payola made a big scandal in recent years. What

would be the word applied if a similar scandal broke out in the following industries: Crayon, TV sets, bootblack, album collectors?

(8) How many phrases can you list which pack infinite wisdom into four simple words. Example: IN GOD WE TRUST. THIS, TOO, SHALL PASS.

(9) How many meaningless phrases can you get which simply switches cliché phrases around on this basis: A chainless end; a pitless bottom.

(10) For a wordy Olympics, how many events can you list such as: Windmill Tilting, Conclusion Jumping.

(11) Try to make up a single, meaningful sentence, in which each word begins with a different letter of the alphabet, starting with "A", and going through to "Z" with the sentence 26 words long.

(12) Take a number of consecutive pages of the dictionary. Then see if you can make a sentence up, making reasonable sense, with the maximum number of alliterative words.

(13) The rhyme: "A thorp . . . Is a dorp" is true, and it makes sense when you look the words up. Can you make up any other similar rhymes with real, screwball words like this —and still make sense.

(14) How many phrases can you list to create new substitutes for the old cliché: "That's the way the cookie crumbles."

(15) If a professor of Music's lectures are "noteworthy," what might be descriptions for lectures in the following subjects: Oceanography, Transportation, Religion, Speech Therapy, Botany, Marriage Counseling, Architecture?

(16) If olfactory is an elderly mill that smells, what is (a) mandate, (b) an intent (c) a porthole?

(17) If you describe plural groups as a "giggle of teenagers" or a "rash of dermatologists", how would you describe similar groups of (a) allergists, (b) surgeons, (c) urologists, (d) ophthalmologists, (e) bacteriologists, (f) laryngologists?

(18) How many words can you list where the first half of the noun is a verb, and the second half, the verb's direct object? (Example: breakfast)

(19) How many words or expressions can you list, one containing the word "up," the other, "down"? (Example: Shut up; pipe down)

(20) Some modern writers of the far-out school claim they get great artistry in their prose by taking a page of a manuscript, folding it down the middle, and matching it up to another page, also folded down the middle, from an entirely different chapter. Take any pages of written material you might find handy—do the same thing—and see what a work of art you get! (Note: Have enough pages of material handy to do this at a party, then have each guest read his result.)

chapter seven

WHAT'S IN A NAME?

Note to Game Maniacs:

How you can resist the metaphysical passion of the reading portion of these chapters is unfathomable, but if you insist, turn to page 103 and try your hand at the game section first. Then you'll have to go through the reading portion anyway to find the answers, if any.

Chester Morris has a long and distinguished career as an actor, but beyond that he has an insatiable curiosity about all the things in life which go to make up brain-twisters. At one time, I received a letter from him mentioning how odd the names of many celebrities seem when their foreshortened or nicknames are omitted. The list he sent along certainly bears his theory out:

Anthony Martin, Daniel Kaye, John Benny, Richard Van-Dyke, John Carson, Michael Rooney, John Paar, Burton Lancaster, Samuel Davis, Jr., Steven Allen, Anthony Curtis, Samuel Levinson, William Cullen, Michael Mantle, Chester Huntley, Yelberton Tittle, Daniel Thomas, Edward Fisher, Abraham Burrows, Andrew Williams, Harry Crosby, Edward Sullivan, Charles Liston, Lawrence Peter Berra, Jerome Lewis, Anthony Randall, etc.

In reading a list like this, you have to pause several times to try to figure out just whom the celebrity is. Conversely, the same puzzlement descends on the score when you take the full name of some well-known names and convert them to nicknames: Win Churchill, Al Schweitzer, Betty Taylor, Al Lunt, Tommy Wolfe, Bert Russell, etc.

As a matter of fact, a Chicago newspaperman by the name of Jack McPhaul found that he had to give up his informal first name in favor of John J. McPhaul for his book *Deadlines and Monkeyshines* because his editors at Prentice-Hall felt "Jack" was too informal for the library trade.

"Maybe they're right," says McPhaul. "Now that I think of it, authors under the names of Chuck Dickens, Hank Thoreau, Wallie Emerson, Andy Gide, Al Dante, or Jackie Keats probably would never have got off the ground."

Robert Conklin claims that this sort of thing has far deeper significance. He claims that the whole tone of history would have been changed if civilization had sailed East instead of West. Famous names of history would read, among others: Mo Ghandi, Wolfie Mozart, Kate the Great, Lenny Vinci, Hank Cinq, Kook Khan, Toot Ankhamen.

Constance Lapham joins in the fun with a suggestion for a game she claims affords amusement on long automobile trips. She finds that reversing the order of famous combinations of names makes them sound so unusual that they are practically unrecognizable: Sullivan and Gilbert, Eve and Adam, Bess and Porgy, Andy and Amos, Remus and Romulus, Hart and Rodgers, Costello and Abbott, Pythias and Damon, Pollux and Castor, Zooey and Franny, Taylor and Lord, Hardy and Laurel.

Alan Whitney has another game he likes to play. He makes up lists of people who are famous by a name other than the one given at birth. Among those he lists are:

Nicholas Bronstein (Douglas Fairbanks)
Lev Bronstein (Leon Trotsky, and no relation)
Elsa Bierbower (Elsie Janis)
Gladys Smith (Mary Pickford)
Mary Ann Evans (George Eliot)
Israel Baline (Irving Berlin)

Princess Alexandrina of Hanover, later Duchess of Kent (Queen Victoria)
Son of Michael—translated (V. Molotov)
Joseph Green—translated (Giuseppe Verdi)
Benjamin Kubelski (Jack Benny)
Albert of Saxe-Coburg (Edward VII)
Michael Goldbogen (Mike Todd)
Archie Leach (Cary Grant)
Bernard Schwartz (Tony Curtis)
William Sidney Porter (O. Henry)
Domenico Teotocopulo (El Greco)

But names have a way of popping up in the oddest places. Philip Cohen, president of Oceana Publications and once an assistant to the law librarian at Columbia University tells me that the professional journal known as *Law and Order Magazine* is published by the Copps Publishing Company. The editor's name, Lee Lawler. And there's an inseparable executive team at the New York City Aquarium named Coates and Atz. Christopher W. Coates is the director of the institution, and James W. Atz is the curator.

Names, of course, are everywhere, and if you keep your eyes open enough, you'll notice some rather odd combinations. Correspondents from many parts of the country have kept me up to date on a variety of combinations designed to make you blink twice:

From Bernice Rowell: A former insurance agency in Rutland, Vermont was Ketcham, Killem, and Burnham.

From Edna Toney: A law office in Gloversville, N. Y. is named Muddle & Muddle.

From Howard Schneid: A law office in Westport, Connecticut sounds like an ad for a savings bank—Wake, See, and Dimes.

From Anita Despres: In Manhattan there is a hospital with three physicians on its staff: Payne, Slaughter, and Killman.

From Norman Hill: In Sault Ste. Marie, Michigan, there

used to be a law firm named Sharp & Handy; an insurance firm named Old & Blank.

From Pauline Robertson: In Amarillo, Texas, there's an undertaker named Boxwell.

From Jean Bassnett: In Buffalo, New York, there's a company named Tinney Cadillac.

From Vera Helper: In Mansfield, Illinois, the head of the school system is Mr. Pound. The initials of his secretary, typed on the bottom of his letters, are "lb."

From Newton Miller: The name of an electrolysis specialist for skin conditions in Rockefeller Center, New York is Harold Noskin.

From Margaret Griffiths: In Baltimore there is a real estate company by the name of Ruff & Brawley.

From Ina Forbus: In Durham, N. C. there are two surgeons, one named Carver, the other Cleaver.

From Earle Douglas: In Dhahran, three American employees at the Ras Tanura Health Center are named Sickman, Aiken, and Paine.

From Ben Hayes: In Columbus, Ohio, a man by the name of Dick House was listed in the telephone directory as House, Dick. He got so many screwball calls that he changed his listing to House, Richard W.

From Ernest Vaughn: At the University of Kentucky, there is an English professor by the name of Charles Dickens.

From Dr. Henry Michelson: In Minneapolis, there was a sign in a store window reading: SAM KLEIN—FORMERLY NANCY LEE.

From Mort Cornin: Two characters in two separate books —*The Port*, by Henry Beetle Hough, and *Vertical and Horizontal*, by Lillian Ross—are both named "Fifield."

From Mrs. M. J. Aber: In the Yellow Pages of the Manhattan Telephone Directory you can find these doctors: Coffin, Console, Cunning, Needleman, Profitt, and Quick.

Names are very interesting when you try to find some common corollary coefficient among several. In other words, what do they have in common? For instance, the names on this list have one very definite thing in common, besides the fact that they are all well-known authors: John Locke, Oliver Goldsmith, Percy Bysshe Shelley, John Keats, Charles Darwin, Oliver Wendell Holmes, William James, Thomas Huxley, Sir Arthur Conan Doyle, Havelock Ellis, Gertrude Stein, Somerset Maugham, Zane Grey, Warwick Deeping, James Joyce, William Carlos Williams, Robinson Jeffers, Michael Arlen, A. J. Cronin, Frank Slaughter.

The answer is, if you haven't already guessed, that each of them was either a full-fledged doctor, or studied medicine seriously in college, with full intent of becoming a doctor of medicine.

Another list which I found interesting is this one: George Washington, Grover Cleveland, James Buchanan, John Adams, Andrew Jackson, Archimedes Zzzyandottie, James Madison, Franklin Pierce. These all have one very definite thing in common. They are all listed in the New York Telephone Directory.

Just to avoid being provincial as far as the East Coast is concerned, I'm obligated to include the list which Sue Cogwill sent me from San Diego. This includes: Bird, Crow, Eagle, Finch, Canary. They are all birds of America, of course. But what else? They are also faculty members listed in the San Diego State College faculty telephone directory.

There's another interesting group of names which W. S. Tracy sent me you may want to mull over: Philip Wylie, Pearl Buck, Art Linkletter, James Baldwin, T. S. Matthews, William Saroyan, Rev. Martin Luther King, Ingmar Bergman, Woodrow Wilson. Aside from the authorship of at least one successful book, these are all children of Protestant ministers.

Author Gerald Raftery, in addition to having his name misspelled more than any other human being, enjoys what he calls Proofreader puns with names which he catches in print on occasion. For instance, he noted that *Newsweek* mentioned that performer Nancy Ames was a graduate of "tony Bennett Junior College", which at the hands of a proofreader came out "Tony Bennett Junior College." Mr. Raftery visualizes other goofs like "Prince Rainier danced with elegant Grace", or more anonymously, "He seized the opportunity with Joy," or "The Senator scathingly denounced this Levy."

Graham Parker has a game which threatens to cause more insomnia, invented by a legal friend of his, who has decorated his apartment with colors he calls Whizzer White, Hugo Black, Willie Maize, John Brown, Ben Blue, Gerald Green, or you-name-it.

As if this isn't bad enough, Frances Holmes has come down with a virus which compels people to invent names where the first and last names mean the same thing: Blanche White, Peter Stone, Rex King, Esther Starr, Stephen Garland. But this correspondent goes even further: The obsessional drive to turn everyone's name into an anagram: "Mrs. *Walsh* lost her *shawl* while walking with Mr. *Foster* in the *forest*."

Arthur Berger is not content with this. He likes to indulge in clerihews, of the following sorts:

John
Was Gay
But Gerard Hopkins
Manley

Dame May
Was Witty
But John Greenleaf
Was Whittier

Oscar
Was Wilde
But Thornton
Was Wilder

Names remind Earl Reese of those whose immortality rests on an untoward action on the part of the doer. He suggests that John Wilkes Booth is remembered as an assassin rather than as an actor; Oscar Wilde is remembered more as a deviate than as a genius; Wrong Way Corrigan would never be remembered as an aviator if he hadn't flown the wrong way; Roy Reigels, who ran 105 yards the wrong way in a Rose Bowl game, will aways be remembered for this in sporting circles; and for that matter, the tower of Pisa wouldn't be half so famous if it were vertical.

Down in Baltimore, Mrs. Edwin Wolf has been developing an "all-girl" baseball team out of some of the rugged gentlemen of baseball who happen to have first names which are anything but rugged.

Her team would include: Nellie Fox, Babe Ruth, Sal Maglie, Lena Styles, Gene Woodling, Gussie Triandos, Elly Howard, Birdie Tebbetts, Connie Mack.

"And," continues Mrs. Wolf, "if you really want to stretch it, you can add Ruby Gomez and Vicki Power."

But Tom Hamilton, casting off the shackles of the Hot Stove League he conducts down in Wise, Virginia, feels that this is not enough. He would form a team with girl-like names, position by position, of real players:

Catcher, Beverly Gooch, Pittsburgh, '27; First Base, Ivy Wingo, Cincinnati, '24; Second Base, Ivoria Layne, Washington, '44; Third Base, Gail Henley, Pittsburgh, '54; Shortstop, Claire Goodwin, Kansas City, '14; Outfield, Alta Cohen, Philadelphia, '33; Shirley Cuyler, Pittsburgh, '25; Pitcher, Vivian Lindaman, Boston, '08.

He continues with an all-girlish *nickname* team which includes Nanny Fernandez, Boston, '42; Liz Funk, Detroit, '30; Lena Blackburn, Chicago, '14—*plus* a team of all-girlish last names, such as Paul Florence, Ernest Shirley, Pete Rose, Martin Marion, all of various major league teams and vintages.

On top of all this, Roger Williams has come up with a new game of his own called "Appropriate Names." His nomination to start the ball rolling:

Phil Linz —— Utility Infielder

But before we leave baseball, we might add that they finally decided *not* to put a dome over the new Shea Stadium because it would shed too many tiers.

While John Pearson was having a bout with the flu in a British Columbia hospital, his temperature of 103 got him started on a game concerning the names of famous people. Before his pulse was back to normal, he had created:

Nice try, Bruce! (Robert)
Follow the arrow, Harold (1066)
Watch your step, Fred (Astaire)
Don't get your wires crossed, Alexander (Bell)
Cut, Ben (Casey)
Mind your head, Charles (the First)
Watch that slice, Jack (the Ripper)

T. E. Farmer is another one who likes to fool around with names. His gambit is to identify the natives of various states and countries in an unlikely manner:

Natives of Florida (Flora)
Natives of Carolina (Carols)
Natives of Maine (Maniacs)
Natives of Colombia (Columbines)
Natives of Nepal (Neapolitans)
Natives of Italy (Italics)
Natives of Bulgaria (Bulges)

In addition, he would list the native of Iceland who emigrated as a de-Icer; the native of Luxembourg who did likewise, de-Luxe.

Even away from the world of brain twisters, there is trouble with names. Out of Dublin comes a story about Jim Geraghty, long the man responsible for the humor and cartoons of *The New Yorker*, and Charles Saxon, one of his best cartoonists. On registering them at a hotel, the Dublin clerk wrote down Mr. Geraghty's name with swiftness and precision. When Mr. Saxon repeated his name for the same procedure, the clerk said: "I beg your pardon, but how do you spell that?"

When you get to names on the television scene, there is no telling what might happen. Bert Granet, however, is able to sum it up in one simple couplet which he dedicates, along with the footnotes, to the F.C.C.:

> Doctor,[1] Lawyer,[2] Indian Chief[3]
> Richman,[4] Poorman,[5] Beggarman,[6] Thief.[7]

For his footnotes, he includes:

[1] Dr. Kildare, Ben Casey, Medic, Young Dr. Malone
[2] Perry Mason, Defenders, Law and Mr. Jones
[3] Broken Arrow, Cochise, Rifleman, Wagon Train
[4] The Millionaire
[5] Beachcombers, Adventures in Paradise
[6] Robin Hood
[7] Untouchables, Detectives, Asphalt Jungle, 87th Precinct.

There are many other respondents who find this kind of small-game hunting with names a rewarding sort of malady.

Charles Mantoni has created a game with names he calls Hollywood. For a film about the sea, for instance, he would cast George Raft, Howard Keel, Ethel Waters, and Clara Bow. For a religious drama, he would cast George Abbott, Thelonius Monk, and Shirley Temple.

Jack Cornwall, however, has his own game of Hollywood. It's called "Columnist," and he creates mythical columns on this order:

"Dinah Shore last week gave a big swim party welcoming Turhan Bey back to Hollywood. Present were Ernie Banks, Larry Rivers, Veronica Lake, Lily Pons, and Geraldine Brooks. It was quite a fling until Gail Storm blew in with Claude Rains, C. P. Snow, and Curt Flood . . . Robert Trout was out on the town last night at the Cape Cod Room with

Saul Bass and Newton Minnow. They were accompanied by
Peter Finch, Dean Martin, Anthony Quayle, and Walter
Pidgeon, all preparing to fly to Miami."

In Cleveland, Ohio, Marion Stewart systematically upsets
her sleeping cart with Unlikely Enterprise names. After a long
drive along commercial strips, she has come up with such
commercial establishments as Hiawatha's Bavarian Hut,
Svenson's Hacienda, Luigi's Igloo, McTavish's Villa, and
Stumpf's Chateau, not to mention O'Rafferty's Hofbrau,
Ginocopoli's Smorgasbord, de Beaupre's Fish and Chips, and
Cassidy's Samovar. Going in a little stronger for her fiendish
contradictions, she has devised such eating spots as Tiny's
Imperial Palace and Thruway-Vue Hideaway.

And just to prove that this sort of thing doesn't have to be
fictional, Kenneth Gompertz reports that there is a shop on
one of Glasgow's main streets called Ziederbaum's Tartans.

I have never seen in a single listing the names of those authors and celebrities who might get confused at a cocktail
party by the time the third martini got around. The list always starts with Sinclair Lewis, Upton Sinclair, Sherwood
Anderson, Robert Sherwood, Maxwell Anderson, C. S. Forester, E. M. Forster, C. S. Lewis, Lewis Mumford, Robert Louis
Stevenson—the list goes on. At such a mythical cocktail party,
the inattentive dilettante or the well-versed cosmopolite
could easily be thrown for a loss.

It wasn't long before I received many suggestions to add
to the list.

Donald Brown would add:

    Laura Z. Hobson
    Zora Neale Hurston
    Winston Churchill
    Winston S. Churchill

This, incidentally, recalls an incident involving both the
Churchills. As the British Churchill began to come into

prominence, he became aware of the American novelist of the same name. He wrote and suggested that the American might want to add a middle initial to his name to avoid confusion. American Novelist Churchill wrote back in no uncertain terms that he had been writing books for a good deal longer than the young Britisher, and that if anyone was to take on an extra initial, it had blasted well better be the gentleman from the east side of the Atlantic. From that moment on, the British statesman signed his books Winston S. Churchill.

But to return to the mythical cocktail party. Mrs. Carl Woodford would add:

Alfred Einstein
Albert Einstein

Ellen Bowman would add a few artists:

Norman Rockwell
Rockwell Kent
Norman Kent

Larry Johnson would add:

John Cecil Holm
John Clellon Holmes
Oliver Wendell Holmes
Tennessee Ernie Ford
Tennessee Williams

Frances Burgasser would add:

Joseph Conrad
Conrad Aiken
Joyce Kilmer
James Joyce
Wendell Phillips
Phillips Brooks
Van Wyck Brooks

Van Wyck Mason
John Mason Brown
Matthew Arnold
Arnold Bennett
Bennett Cerf
Bertrand Russell
J. Russell Lowell
Lowell Thomas
Jane Austen
Jane Austin

Jean Vermes would like to create a breezier party with:

Zona Gale
Gloria Gale
Storm Jameson
Theodor Storm
Nancy Hale
Edward Everett Hale
William MacLeod Raine
Edgar Parks Snow
Wilbert Snow
John Blow
Wyndham Lewis

To complete the most totally confused cocktail party of all time, Bob Niedelman of Sussman & Sugar, publishers' advertising agency, starts the finish off in this way:

"The identities of authors we're chatting with are not only confused and confounded, but curiously mismated as well.

"We have just turned away from Robert Louis Stevenson, Robert Lewis Taylor, and Robert Lewis Shayon to greet Taylor and Erskine Caldwell; Flannery and Frank O'Connor; Nancy and Angus Wilson Ross; Betty and Robert Paul Smith; Rebecca and Nathaniel West; Virginia and Thomas Wolfe, and, of course, the Duke and Kathleen Winsor—not to mention those two titans of literature we found while reaching for our seventh gin: Henry James Joyce and Upton Sinclair Lewis Carroll."

Ed Fuller, who does a lot of theatrical casting, finally helps us to close the party up before it gets totally out of hand. "I'm sort of toying with the idea," he says, "of throwing a party for quite a few people I'd like to introduce to each other at one time. These include: Oona O'Neill, Una Merkel, Ona Munson, Osa Massen, Uta Hagen, and Ulla Jacobson!"

If names have their place in reality, they also have a magnificent reservation set aside for them in fantasy. Dr. Ted Kaufman and Chuck Israels have worked out a list of names which can take their place in history for obvious reasons:

Xavier Greenstamps
Tyrone Shoelaces
Russell Upsomegrub
Amanda B. Reckonedwith
Bertha D. Blues
Abner Selfaball
Ensign Sear
Sharon Sharealike
Rachel Prejudice
Sybil Rights
Freida Slaves
Gustav Wind
Norman Conquest
Noah Vale
Warren Peace
Helen Highwater
Justin D. Nickatime
Lois and Carmen Denominator
Orlando D. Free
Homer D. Brave
Sally Forth

Baron Waste
Walter Wallcarpet
Linus Busy
Celia Fate
Paddy O'Furniture
Sonia Papermoon

Way down yonder in New Orleans, Rosemary Corry tells me that the members of Le Petit Théâtre du Vieux Carré lighten their rehearsal waiting time by creating all kinds of star names for the Laughing Stock Company, as their mythical group is named. As soon as a medical play comes their way, they plan to feature such stars as Anna Syn, Sue Chur, Sally Patica, Cora Seedin, and the Attricks brothers, Jerry and Petey.

What's more, they've lined up some occupational characters whose shingles could well adorn any office building:

Lawyers: Judge Knott, Lester B. Judge
Caterers: Toomney Cook, "Spa" La Brotte
Auto Salesmen: Oscar Mann, Hone Swann
Divorce lawyers: Hugo Urway, Olga Myne

One player, in between curtain calls, utilized her role as Socrates's wife by creating the rallying call for the group: "Xanthippe Canoe and Tyler, too!"

Mrs. Corry is not content to stop there. Her list of leading men for potential casting includes Scott Free, Steele Wool, Cliff Hanger, Rock Bottom, Peck Toral, Bunker Hill, Hi Colonic, Benny Dick Teen, and the suitor who never gets his girl: Luke Warm.

Among the ingenues and sex symbols, she includes "Kitten" Kaboodle, Pat Pending, Rose Beef, Stark Nekkid and Bessie Mae Mucho. We will pause, mercifully, at this list, but if you should visit Le Petit Théâtre in New Orleans, we know that Mrs. Corry would have more for you.

Not to be outdone, Hugh Uhlmann, president of the

Standard Milling Company in Kansas City has designed a method to extract names which sound like movie stars among eminent composers. He includes Rock Mananoff, as the curly-headed hero; Chi Kowsky, the gangster; Moe Zart, the producer; and the famous lady dress designer from Norway, Mrs. Bea Thoeven.

Bernice Bender, from out Chicago way, can't sit still when activity like this is going on. She attributes that group of people known as Benny Diction, Arch Bishop, Gloria N. Exsellsis, Kathy Drill, Bea Attitude, and Jenny Siss to a local church group.

To a cooking school faculty, she assigns Hazel Nutt, Sterling Silver, Chuck Roast, and Minnie Stroney.

After all this attention to the world of names, fanciful and otherwise, we might beat our way back to the world of reality with an event which actually happened not too long ago. A waiter at the luxurious Chambord served an entire family, including a child of four, with as much attention to the child as to the rest of the family. The child, completely stunned with such ubiquitous solicitude, remarked: "He thinks I'm real."

GAMES FOR CHAPTER SEVEN

At a gathering, have each person make a list of three celebrities, using their full names rather than the customary and recognized nickname. Each person reads his list, one name at a time. The others in the gathering must respond quickly to what the person is: Comedian, actor, prizefighter, etc. The first one to come out with the correct classification is the winner. Example: Lawrence Peter Berra, Jerome Lewis, Anthony Randall. (Note: Anyone with half a feather for a brain can classify these names if they're allowed to think about it. Therefore, this has to be done on a flash reaction basis, or it's too simple.)

Conversely, follow the same pattern, with each member of the gathering making a list of three well-known names with a nickname rather than a customary full, formal name. As each person reads his list to the group, others must respond on a flash-reaction basis. The first one reacting, of course, wins the round. (Example: Wallie Emerson, Jackie Keats, Betty Taylor.)

In the same manner, have each person write down a famous team in reverse order. The first person in the group to raise his hand must identify the team. (Example: Bess and Porgy, Hart and Rodgers, Zooey and Franny.)

For a solitaire game of above, make a list of each category and see how many you can get. Score:

For real names instead of nicknames:

Excellent   15
Good   10
Fair   5

For nicknames instead of real names:

Excellent   10
Good   8
Fair   6

For switching well-known teams:

Excellent   10
Good   8
Fair   6

Find the well-known name of the following people whose names at birth were:

Nicholas Bronstein
Lev Bronstein
Elsa Bierbower
Gladys Smith
Mary Ann Evans
Israel Baline
Princess Alexandrina of Hanover, later Duchess of Kent
Son of Michael (translated)
Joseph Green (translated)
Benjamin Kubelski
Albert of Saxe-Coburg
Michael Goldbogen
Archie Leach
Bernard Schwartz
William Sidney Porter
Domenico Teotocopulo

Excellent   6
Good   4
Fair   2

For a purely personal game, make a list of the odd combinations of names you might find (a) on business signs, (b) driving along highways, (c) browsing through a phone book or yellow pages. (You'll have to score yourself on this one)

Find the common corollary coefficient of the following names: (In other words, what do they have in common besides writing)

Percy Bysshe Shelley, John Keats, Charles Darwin, Oliver Wendell Holmes, William James, Thomas Huxley, Sir Arthur Conan Doyle, Havelock Ellis, Gertrude Stein, Somerset Maugham, Zane Grey, Warwick Deeping, James Joyce, William Carlos Williams, Robinson Jeffers, Michael Arlen, A. J. Cronin, Frank Slaughter.

(Score: If you get it, you're good)

In the same manner, figure out what the following have in common: George Washington, Grover Cleveland, James Buchanan, John Adams, Andrew Jackson, Archimedes Zzzyandottie, James Madison, Franklin Pierce.

(Score: If you get it, you're a total genius)

Aside from the authorship of at least one successful book, the following have another very prominent thing in common: Philip Wylie, Pearl Buck, Art Linkletter, James Baldwin, T. S. Matthews, William Saroyan, Rev. Martin Luther King, Ingmar Bergman, Woodrow Wilson.

(Score: If you get this, you're pretty damn well-informed)

Make up a list of journalistic descriptions, which can backfire by making a proper name out of the adjectives: (Examples: Prince Rainier danced with elegant Grace; He seized the opportunity with Joy)

Excellent   5
Good   3
Fair   1

Make up a list of new color modes, based on the names of real people. (Example: Hugo Black, Ben Blue)

Excellent   3
Good   2
Fair   1

If you're utter idiot enough to like anagrams, how many sentences can you make up with proper names involved like this example: "Mrs. *Walsh* lost her *shawl* while walking with Mr. *Foster* in the *forest*."

Since I, personally, could never do an anagram or cross-word puzzle of any kind, I will grade this with total prejudice:

Excellent   0

A "clerihew" is a biographical quatrain, as in this example:

Oscar
Was Wilde
But Thornton
Was Wilder

Got any more at home like this? If you have at least one more, you move to the top of the class.

John Wilkes Booth is remembered as an assassin rather than an actor. How many other names, places or figures of prominence or notoriety are known for their misdeeds rather than their deeds?

Excellent   3
Good   2
Fair   1

How many baseball players can you name with girlish names or nicknames. (Examples: Babe Ruth, Connie Mack)

Excellent 15
Good 10
Fair 5

"Appropriate Names" is a game which is just now being developed. (Example: Phil Linz—Utility Infielder)

If you can name any more, you'll become a charter member of the "Appropriate Name" Club, because no one else has yet named another.

Combining a slang cliché with a famous first name, how many of the following can you guess? Example: (Watch your step, Fred *Astaire*.)

Nice try, Bruce ——
Follow the arrow, Harold ——
Don't get your wires crossed, Alexander ——
Cut, Ben ——
Mind your head, Charles ——
Watch that slice, Jack ——

Grade yourself or your friends 5 points for each blank filled in.

Excellent 25 points
Good 20 points
Fair 15 points

Now, turn right around and try to make up some more.

Excellent 5 more
Good 3 more
Fair 2 more

If natives of Florida are called Flora, what would be an equally appropriate name for the natives of the following: Carolina, Maine, Colombia, Nepal, Italy, Bulgaria. Score: No official score on this one. It's too easy.

Take the following famous line, and find at least one television show to go with each category:

Doctor, lawyer, Indian chief
Richman, poorman, beggarman, thief

No official score, because if you watch television it's your own fault, and if you don't watch it, you wouldn't know.

The following are really games to put yourself to sleep with, or keep yourself awake with, or torment or pacify yourself with, and again there is no official scoring. However, with a little ingenuity, you can drive your guests off their rockers by trying to compile several of these ideas:

(1) What other famous actors would you cast for a drama about the sea, starring George Raft and Howard Keel?

(2) You are writing a Hollywood column. If it's a swim party given by Dinah Shore for Turhan Bey, what other stars would you include to provide more water, storms, fish and birds?

(3) How many Unlikely Roadside Enterprises can you name like Hiawatha's Bavarian Hut and O'Rafferty's Hofbrau?

(4) In the most confused cocktail party of all times, what other names would you invite besides Sinclair Lewis, Upton Sinclair, Sherwood Anderson, Robert Sherwood, C. S. Forester, E. M. Forster, C. S. Lewis, Lewis Mumford, and others?

(5) How many couples—quite unlikely ones—would you include at the same party besides Taylor and Erskine Caldwell, Virginia and Thomas Wolfe?

(6) How many names could you possibly put together like: Xavier Greenstamps, Tyrone Shoelaces, Lois and Carmen Denominator?

(7) How many firms can you make up like the Divorce

Lawyers: Hugo Urway, Olga Myne; or the regular lawyers: Judge Knott, Lester B. Judge?

(8) How much sleep are you going to get tonight after reading all this?

chapter eight

NOSE FOR NEWS

Note to Game Maniacs:

If a reporter stepped up to you and said "I'm Cutt —from the *Blade*," what would you do? If you want to get right into the games here, turn to page 120, and pick up the rest of the fun later. If you're still sane.

Newspapers will be with us always, offering a fertile field to the lynx-eyed reader who likes to find the gems hidden in typo's, double meanings, and hilarious goofs in print.

One of the most poignant clippings I've received comes from Eric Nelson, who sent me this classified ad from a Seattle paper:

FOR SALE: Complete skydiving equipment. Used only once.

Another fascinating advertisement comes from James Birnberg, who spotted this in a Berkeley, California paper:

THE LENNOX PHOTOSTATIC SERVICE— THE MODERN WAY TO REPRODUCE

R. W. Batchelder has also unearthed a classified gem in the Hackettstown, N. J. paper:

WANTED—Young female to model in the nude for life painting group. Phone 425-5592 for inspection.

The parade of unlikely goofs in the press is endless, regardless of where you live in the country:

From Harry Wade, in New Orleans, an ad:

RELIGIOUS ARTICLES AND PRALINES

From Mary Ellen Quinn in Sloatsburg, N. Y., an ad for an antique shop, with the headline: JUNQUE.

From Ross King, in Hudson, New York, a classified ad:

> YARDS AND CELLARS CLEANED
> AND HAULED AWAY.

From Richard Nagy, in Bloomfield, N. J., an advertisement:

7 nights . . . 8 days in Puerto Rico . . . also available: Share-a-room plan for single men and women.

From Mrs. Lee Yudin, in Philadelphia, an ad:

NOW PLAYING—"COMMON LAW WIFE" If you are old enough to be married, you must see it. If you are not old enough to be married, you cannot see it. Children Under 12 Free.

From G. Harris Danzberger, in Hingham, Mass., an ad:

PART TIME WOMAN WANTED

From C. T. Robinson, in Weston, Conn., an ad:

NOW PLAYING—
HIGHLY RECOMMENDED—LOSS OF INNOCENCE

From Jerry Warwin, in Rochester, N. Y., an entertainment headline:

JUNO AND THE PAYCHECK

From Alan Garfinkel, in Champaign, Ill., an ad:

> NOW PLAYING:
> THE CHILDREN'S HOUR
> NOT FOR CHILDREN

From Dorothy Russell, in Milan, Ohio, an ad from a yarn-maker:

BE SURE TO PURCHASE ENOUGH YARN TO FINISH YOUR ARTICLE BEFORE YOU START

From Karen Steinberg, an ad:

EARLY AMERICAN STONEWARE BY CONTEMPORARY CERAMICS

From Max Senopky, a mattress ad:

ASK ABOUT OUR LAY-AWAKE PLAN

From Betty Frazier in Fort Worth, Texas, a news item:

"County commissioners agreed Monday to name the Tarrant County convention center the Tarrant County Convention Center."

From Robert Wasdon, in Tampa, a classified ad:

SACRIFICE: 4 CEMETERY LOTS.
OWNERS MOVED.

From Gypsy Wilson, in Pineville, Ky., a news item:

"The bride was of steel and was posted for a load limit of 12 tons."

From Burt Kaufman, in Boston, a headline:

REVOLT IN BRUSSELS SPROUTS

(Note: This is *not* verified)

From Lorna Tracy, in New York City, an ad:

RED BARN COIN-O-MATIC LAUNDROMAT
Under New Management—We have an attendant on hand to remove your clothes while you shop.

And from a farmer's trade paper, Elizabeth Smith sends us from Kennett Square, Pennsylvania, an advertisement which has neither typo nor double meaning, but does have a charm all its own:

> BIN BOOT BUMPER. Unit automatically thumps bulk bin boot while unloading auger rungs, preventing bridging. Bumper jars side of boot with slow, measured beat, assuring feed-down. Runs on standard 115-volt current.

Writes Mrs. Smith: "How long has it been since *your* bulk bin boot has been beaten and bumped by the bin boot bumper?"

Activity in the nation's press is hard to keep up with. For instance, Margaret Park sent me a headline from the Memphis *Commercial Appeal* regarding a story about local beer permits. The headline: JUDGE SITS ON EXPLOSIVE BEER CASE.

Ron Policy sent along a clipping from the Akron *Beacon-Journal* which points out that the U. S. Bureau of Printing and Engraving made a typographical error in several thousand dollar bills. The story quotes a Bureau spokesman as saying: "A very tragic erros."

The Kalamazoo *Gazette* is not without its problems. Rita Hardy discovered a want ad clipped from that paper, asking for a registered nurse. "To work in a nursing home," the ad reads. "Good wakes."

From Florida State University, Marie Williams sent in a classified ad reading: "WANTED: Small green frogs such as are found on widows at night. Call Dept. of Biological Sciences."

The members of the Fourth Estate may go forth with a fifth under their arms, but they are a stalwart crew, and we couldn't do without them. In their honor, Bruce Fessenden, of Harrisburg, Pennsylvania, dropped me a line to recall a journalistic game with endless possibilities. It's a list of self-introductions as practiced by would-be news reporters:

I'm Brown, from the *Sun*.
I'm Alice, from the *Mirror*.
I'm Cutt, from the *Blade*.
I'm Justice, from the *Tribune*.
I'm Tied, from the *Post*.

As usual, a game like this is dangerous to mention in TRADE WINDS. The ink in the *Saturday Review* of that week had hardly dried before the mail began coming in:

From E. P. H. James:
I'm Ugley, from the *American*
I'm Shakespeare, from the *Globe*
I'm Trumpett, from the *Herald*
I'm Axel, from the *Journal*
I'm Petty, from the *Picayune*
I'm Key, from the *Telegraph*
I'm Change, from the *Times*
I'm Turner, from the *World*

From L. W. Worcester:
I'm Light, from the *Beacon*
I'm Fellow, from the *Traveller*
I'm Keene, from the *Observer*
I'm Summer, from the *Patriot*
I'm A. C., from the *Courant*
I'm Passen, from the *Review*
I'm Dawn, of the *New Era*
I'm Bright, from the *Outlook*
I'm Elder, from the *Statesman*
I'm Morse, from the *Telegraph*
I'm Blood, from the *Scimitar*
I'm Blast, from the *Bugle*
I'm Home, of the *Mountain Eagle*
I'm Sargeant, of the *Guard*
I'm Bilder, of the *Empire*

From Harold F. Smith:
   I'm Farr, from the *Globe*
   I'm Twinkle, from the *Star*
   I'm Tales, from the *Chronicle*
   I'm Steno, from the *Transcript*
   I'm Hoarse, from the *Call*

From Ted Schulz:
   I'm Cash, from the *Register*

From Bob Busby:
   I'm Hitch, of the *Post*
   I'm Power, of the *Press*
   I'm Rise, of the *Mercury*
   I'm Pony, of the *Express*
   I'm Cross, of the *Examiner*
   I'm Hasty, of *Look*
   I'm Mann, of the *World*
   I'm Carrier, of the *Mail*
   I'm Brief, of the *Item*
   I'm Lower, of the *Standard*
   I'm Wilde, of the *Call*
   I'm Ferry, of *Harpers*
   I'm Depth, of the *Atlantic*
   I'm Follower, of the *Leader*
   I'm Tired, of *Life*
   I'm Miss Leading, of the *Advertiser*
   I'm Judge, of the *Advocate*

From Candy Tuttle:
   Trotter, of the *Globe*
   Art, of the *Graphic*
   Wheary, of the *Traveller*

From Olive Corwin:
   Call, of the *Clarion*
   Paine, of the *Citizen*
   Case, of the *Dispatch*

From Rabbi Charles Kroloff:
Broken, of the *Record*
Moon, of the *Sun*

From Tom Murphy:
Preamble, of the *Constitution*
Whom, of the *Inquirer*
Bertha, the *Nation*
Friday, of the *Saturday Review*

From Emmett Peter, Jr.:
Bright, of the *Beacon*
March, of *Time*

From an anonymous note:
Girley, from the *Call*
Pance, from the *Press*
Lowe, from *Life*
Hamm, from the *Digest*
Brand, from the *Standard*
Card, from the *Plain Dealer*
Flunk, from the *Examiner*

From Janet Wolfe:
Abreast, of the *Times*
Behind, of the *Times*

On top of all this, Jack Gardner would establish a Fullertzer Prize, which would be awarded to Tarzan, of the AP.

And, not content to let good baseball players sleep, Jane Fleischman of Santa Monica, would compose an All-Something team, who step to the microphone and announce themselves as:

Scalped, from the Indians
Holey, from the White Sox
Tenor, from the Mets
Chicken, from the Braves

Loot, from the Pirates
Shot, from the Colts

So when you pick up your evening paper, keep all this in mind. Who knows, you may run into the nervous cub reporter who was called into the City Editor's office for a check up on his progress to date. Embarrassed by the cold, silent glare of his boss, the cub sauntered toward the window in the office, where the setting sun was sinking below the purple skies, as they sat in the travelogues.

Fishing for something, *anything*, to say, the reporter looked at the setting sun and asked: "I see your window has a western exposure, doesn't it?"

"If it doesn't," said the City Editor, "it's the best damn news story you've ever had in your hands."

GAMES FOR CHAPTER EIGHT

If you happen to be lining up a dinner party for the coming week, why not make things a little tough. Demand one of the following as the price of admission, which each guest must read at the table that night:

(1) An actual want ad as crazy as:

FOR SALE: Complete skydiving equipment. Used only once.

Or (2) An actual headline as ridiculous as:

JUDGE SITS ON EXPLOSIVE BEER CASE

Or (3) A local sign, company or combination which might liven up the dinner table.

If you should lose all your friends as a result of this, no liability is accepted on this end.

In place of this, furnish your guests with sheets of paper listing the following: (If you'd rather play this solitaire, a score follows for either game)
(Example:

I'm Cutt, from the *Blade*
I'm Behind, from the *Times*)

I'm —— from the *American*
I'm —— from the *Globe*

I'm —— from the *Herald*
I'm —— from the *Sun*
I'm —— from the *Mirror*
I'm —— from the *Post*
I'm —— from the *Picayune*
I'm —— from the *Telegraph*
I'm —— from the *World*
I'm —— from the *Beacon*
I'm —— from the *Traveller*
I'm —— from the *Observer*
I'm —— from the *Courant*
I'm —— from the *Outlook*
I'm —— from the *Bugle*
I'm —— from the *Star*
I'm —— from the *Chronicle*
I'm —— from the *Call*
I'm —— from the *Register*
I'm —— from the *Press*
I'm —— from the *Mercury*
I'm —— from the *Record*
I'm —— from the *Constitution*

Excellent   12
Good   10
Fair   8

Add one point for each newspaper not listed here.

For a reverse game of the above, either as solitaire or as a group game, take the following list and see what you can do with it:

I'm March, of ——
I'm Friday, of the ——
I'm Bertha, of the ——
I'm Whom, of the ——
I'm Preamble, of the ——

I'm Twinkle, of the ——
I'm Broken, of the ——
I'm Paine, of the ——
I'm Wheary, of the ——
I'm Hoarse, from the ——
I'm Fellow, of the ——

Excellent   5
Good   4
Fair   3

Add one point for your own complete originals.

chapter nine

OCCUPATIONAL HAZARDS

Note to Game Maniacs:

The games for this chapter begin on page 129. Cheaters may scan the reading portion of the chapter if they care to, keeping in mind that neither Macbeth nor Lady Macbeth could get away with guilty consciences, though both of them were strong of will.

As usual, this started with a letter. It looked innocent enough when it arrived, and I'm sure Marian Forer, who wrote it, had no Machiavellian scheme in mind. But she unleashed a torrent of reaction which is destined to cause the U. S. Department of Labor to revise its entire concept of job definitions and to cause all those concerned with pension and retirement plans to seek cover.

"I was struck lightly," Mrs. Forer writes, "by the following wonder: If lawyers are disbarred, and priests are unfrocked, how might people in other walks of life be read out of their profession or calling? It occurred to me then that electricians get delighted, that poultry farmers are delayed, and musicians possibly denoted. If these assumptions are correct, surely it follows that cowboys must be deranged, that models are deposed, and judges are obviously distorted. A medium who loses her license is dispirited (and who wouldn't be?). I am told that a messenger is dissented, while a dressmaker gets unbiased. It seems only poetic justice then that an executioner should be decapitated, and it is also possible that if a jeweller becomes dilapidated, that a Far Easterner who is banished is therefore disoriented. I could go on and on, but I don't want to overload the mail handlers. An office worker who can't cope may, alas, become defiled."

For the purpose, then, of establishing a new code book for those who get sacked from their professions, or who wish to retire, we list the other possibilities.

From Alan Littman:
   Moonshiners are distilled
   Bankers are disinterested
   Butchers are delivered
   Models are denuded
   Musicians are decomposed
   Castles are demoted
   Dresses are depleted
   Church windows are distained
   Speak-easies are disjointed

From Donald Holroyd:
   Surveyors are dislocated
   Accountants are disfigured
   Track men are defeated
   Witch doctors are dispelled
   Elementary teachers are degraded
   Train inspectors are derailed

From Dr. George McGeary:
   Symphony conductors are disconcerted
   A Poet Laureate is defrosted
   Tarzans are denatured
   Airforce generals are debased
   Nudists are disarrayed
   Siamese twins are departed
   Obstetricians are degenerated
   Diplomats are disconsolate
   Religious fanatics are detracted
   Cannibal victims are disheartened

Ministers are demoralized
Goldwater is denominated
Orchestra leaders are disbanded

From John F. Wells:
Winemakers are deported
Credit managers are discharged
Phone operators are disconnected
Mathematicians are discounted
Actors are unattended
Politicians are unspeakable

From Dr. Herbert Notkin:
Advertisers are declassified
Witches are disenchanted
Martians are unearthed
Laundresses are depressed
Violinists are unstrung
Musicians are disconcerted
Ball players are debased
Admirals are abridged
Poker players are unstacked
Tailors are unsuited
Arbitrators are undecided
Neurologists are unnerved
A movie actor is depicted

From Carol Rees:
Hotel managers are dislodged
Brides are dismissed
Pig farmers are disgruntled
Butchers are mistaken
Clergymen are demoralized
Committees get disappointed
Electricians get discharged
Welders get disjointed
Flirts get decoyed
Authors are described

From Ralph B. Earle, Jr.:
Ballet dancers are debarred
Choristers are unsung
Fishermen are debated
Pornographers are deluded
Mathematicians are non-plussed
Barbers are departed
Cooks are deserted
Helen was destroyed
Politicians are devoted
Noblemen are discounted
Calendar makers are dismayed
Hairdressers are distressed
Bakers are unrolled
Tree surgeons are uprooted
A lady rain maker is poly-unsaturated
The gunsmith—just plain fired

From Janet Mendell:
Prisoners are excelled
Bridge players are discarded
Charwomen are expunged
Pen manufacturers are disappointed
Teachers are outclassed

From Charles Matheny:
Meteorologists are disgusted
Innkeepers are debunked
Plumbers are discommoded

From Walter Leight:
Farmers are distilled
Turkey stuffers are undressed
Waiters are deserved
Judges are defined
Eulogists are distributed
Intelligence agents are despised

Sailors are discussed
Puzzlers should be dissolved

From Jack Prelentsky:
Dentists are decayed
Clubs are dismembered
Private eyes are undetected
Tennis players are unloved and defaulted
Barmen are distended
Botanists are deflowered
Guides are detoured
Arsonists are unmatched (or fired!)
Postmen are unzipped

Fortunately, Norman Chansky helps us bring all this to a merciful close. He applies this theory of occupational zaniness to the manner in which some of these people might respond to a miserable cold or a virus infection: The short order cook feels waffle; the poet, verse; and the butcher, wurst. The equestrian is hoarse. The gardener has worms, but the football player passes out. The phone operator has ringing in her ears; the mailman is a carrier. The barber feels heady. And the minister incants: "Thy rods and thy staph are of no comfort!"

The gruelling answer for recovery, Mr. Chansky adds, is chicken soup. Then the upholsterer recovers, the luggage salesman loses his grippe, the musician is fit as a fiddle, and the sculptor feels marblous.

GAMES FOR CHAPTER NINE

If lawyers are disbarred and priests are unfrocked, how many fractured ways can you figure out for those of other callings to be read out of their professions? Examples: Electricians are delighted; musicians are decomposed; winemakers are deported. DO NOT CONSULT A DICTIONARY, UNLESS YOU ARE LILY-LIVERED.

Excellent 20
Good 15
Fair 10

From the following list, fill in the blanks as above:

———— are delighted
———— are delayed
———— are denoted
———— are deranged
———— are distilled
———— are delivered
———— are disfigured
———— are degraded
———— are debased
———— are demoralized
———— are depressed
———— are disconcerted
———— are unstacked
———— are unnerved
———— are debarred

——————— are debated
——————— are non-plussed
——————— are devoted
——————— are discounted
——————— are distressed
——————— are unrolled

Excellent   18
Good   15
Fair   12

chapter ten

OCTOPUS AU GRATIN,
OR HOW TO COOK YOUR OWN GOOSE

Note to Game Maniacs:

There is food for thought here, but it might be slightly indigestible. Please do not attempt the game portion of this chapter (page 142) unless you have an adequate supply of bicarbonate on hand. You'll be better off just browsing through the reading portion of the chapter, if you can call it that.

Boone's Restaurant, on the waterfront in Portland, Maine, not only serves delicious lobster, it also provides for its clients a mock menu which can startle any unsuspecting diner.

Offered in sober typeface, in realistic menu fashion, are: Assorted cuts, with iodine ($.80); roast Maine seagull enciente, overstuffed ($2.50); rubber bands and meat ball, with tomato sauce ($.75); fricassee of adolescent wolf, with wild oats ($15.50); young whale stuffed with new Buick ($3500); young whale, stuffed with '37 Ford ($86, including license plate); octopus au gratin with apple in mouth (for eight, $400); roast suckling pig, with bottle, nipple, and Simulac ($2.25); sirloin snake, per foot ($.89); crêpe suzettes, with fire extinguisher ($2.50).

And in the ready-to-take-home department, the menu offers canned clam wings and dehydrated Sebago Lake water —just add water and serve.

This, of course, is a gag menu. But you don't need to look far for *real* menus which are garnished with more decoration than you'll find on an eight-foot wedding cake. As a matter of fact, aspirants to a creative writing career no longer need to confine themselves to books, magazines, stage and films. They can, if they are of such a mind, join the swelling ranks of menu writers who, in a high state of exaltation, reach up into Olympian ether to describe the succulent quality of their favorite nectar or ambrosia.

I talked one time to a man who did nothing else but create these elevated menus, and goes at this thing as he would plunge into a course in fine arts.

"You've got to get their taste buds tingling," Percy Pinsker told me at his office in the Gaylord Printing Company in New York. "Everything today is psychological. Any printer can print a menu. But few know how to make it sing."

One of the earliest pioneers in gilding the menu is Toffenetti's, the restaurant chain which can make a simple and unassuming Idaho potato seem like a full-course meal.

"Toffenetti presents to you," says one of the menus, "the quintessence of entrancing mealiness and fabulous health with his GENUINE IDAHO BAKED POTATOES."

The menu then goes on to say: "Upon that abundant land of Idaho, once upon a time, nature unleashed her fury with moving glaciers, floods, and volcanoes. Today after centuries of quiet, we harvest for you the most beautiful potatoes especially adapted because of their mealiness for baking. So, you who seek health and pleasure come to us and: Just say Idaho."

"A lot of people say our menus are corny," says Pat Coscette, manager of Toffenetti's highly successful shop in New York, "but they work."

Another glorifier of the menu is Ben Wallach, who helps put together the menus for Cobb's Corner in Manhattan. Some of his menus refer to shish-kabob as ". . . roast in the Pit, Blushing Pink Fingers of the Finest Sirloin Steak. Tenderly Roasted on a Steel Skewer, with Jumbo Mushroom Caps and Red Ripe California Tomatoes . . . Served on a Bed of French Fried Idaho Potatoes."

"We like to be different," says Mr. Wallach. "A menu like this takes the customer's mind off waiting. We give them a glass of iced, pure water to keep them busy physically—and a menu to keep them busy mentally."

When I asked him about an item called "Virginny ham," Mr. Wallach said: "Anybody can say 'Virginia.' We say 'Virginny.' It makes us more distinctive."

And it must. Cobb's restaurants have grown as fast as Idaho potatoes, all over New York.

Sometimes menu writers are carried away by their own success. Up in Martha's Vineyard, the Navigator Room of the Harborside Inn lists its mouth-watering dishes with enthusiasm and color. Beef is never simply "roasted." It is listed as "Roast Prime Ribs of Beef Fit for a King"—and $5.25. On the next line, however, you read that the King Size (with the bone) will run you $5.75. This leaves the initial listing of Roast Beef open to question. Is it really fit for a king if it has to be buttressed by the King Size slice for fifty cents additional?

When it comes to king-sized menus, some of the most lavish restaurants also supply the largest-sized menus. The menu of the famous Forum of the Twelve Caesars measures 17 inches by 26 inches, complete with purple ribbon, gold sealing wax, and a gold-embossed logo on the front. At the top of the list of provocative food items is a quotation of Catullus: "Cenabis Bene . . . Apud Me," suggesting to the patron that "You will dine well at my table."

And you will. Here you can dine on anything from "Great Mushrooms stuffed with Snails and Gallic Cheese" to a "Pheasant of the Golden House on a Silver Shield in Gilded Plumage, Roast with an Exquisite Sauce." These items alone would run the check for two of you up to $19.70, without extras.

The Mermaid Tavern in Stratford, Connecticut, run by the same organization, has a menu flavored with the days of Shakespeare. It includes "Chyken Livers Simmered in Sherris Sack" and "Eggs Served wyth Shredded Taters." You won't find a business man's luncheon here—but you will find a suggestion for "the Man of Commerce."

One New York restaurant prints a special St. Patrick's Day menu in green, and manages to come up with a fine melting-pot assortment of items. It's the Hyde Park Restaurant under the genial direction of Larry Lowenstein.

On this day, he features on his menu such dishes as "Erin-Ga-Bragh Cheese Blintzes," "O'Lowenstein's Old Irish Recipe for Corned Beef and Cabbage," and "O'Malley's Kosher Style Knackwurst." In addition, he throws in "Bridey Murphy's Fricassee of Young Spring Chicken."

Some menu showmanship started quite by accident. Thus The Woodlawn, in Madison, Connecticut, hands out real miniature blackboards to its diners—the result of losing its ace typist unexpectedly. And Percy Pinsker discovered that one of his clients, a Spanish restaurant known as Liborio, had trouble explaining what each Spanish dish was. He stumbled on the idea of putting the price in the middle, the Spanish dish on the left, and the English translation on the right. Business went up twenty-five per cent. He also discovered that culture pays off. One of his menus is laced with quotes by Emerson, Wilde, Ibsen, Twain, Milton, and Rabelais.

The Waldorf cafeteria chain is now discovering that old-style cafeterias are dimming in popularity; the chain is experimenting with neat, moderately priced restaurants whose menus offer dishes from "The Iron Oven," the "Soup Cauldron," and the "Sandwich Block."

But not all successful restaurants are succumbing to the trend. Chock Full O'Nuts is growing by logarithms and still lists a sliced ham and cheese sandwich as just that. Fruit cup is fruit cup. Chocolate cake is chocolate cake.

But even in this oasis of simplicity, the temptation is too strong to resist. The coffee is listed as "heavenly" coffee.

On the West Coast, Jane Williams reports that the coffee shops there provide some rare copy. The Golden Cup will serve you "The Sultan—65¢—Lush Opulence of Double-Rich

Chocolate—on Chocolate Sundae, Crowned with an Himalayan Swirl of Snowy Whipped Cream, a Handful of Nut Nuggets and Gemmed with a Ruby-Red Maraschino Cherry."

The Copper Penny has a dinner salad that is "Tossed just as high as the regular salad, caught in a smaller bowl."

The International House of Pancakes offers Brazilian Banana Pancakes that are "exciting as a tango."

A chain of hot dog stands features such items as Dandy Danes, Bashful Bassets.

At Woody's SmorgasBurger Restaurants, "MountainBurgers" are offered—for those who think and eat Big.

We also have word that the Holiday Inn in Indianapolis carried a sign one time: ATTEND THE CHURCH OF YOUR CHOICE—SMORGASBORD TODAY.

Another tide of verbiage flooding the land is the naming of various cocktail lounges found in hotel rooms. A game has sprung up among traveling drummers which consists of unlikely names for the lounges at various hotels throughout the country.

For the sake of cluttering up your mind a little more, here are some of the suggestions:

The Straightjacket Room at the Bellevue
The Cloak Room at the Raleigh
The Generator Room at the Edison
The Handwriting Room at the Palmer House
The Steam Room at the Fulton
The Cracker Room at the Ritz
The Slip Room at the Barbizon
The Powder Room at the Dupont

As usual, when this appeared in TRADE WINDS, various readers responded admirably:

The Bottoms-Up Room at the Breakers
   (Brad Boynton)
The Commodore Room at the Vanderbilt
   (Priscilla Whiley)

The Which One? Room at the Roosevelt
  (Charles Arnold)
The Barber Room at the Seville
  (Wray Congdon)
The Hanger Room at the Clift
  (Vivian Breckenfield)
The Drew Room at the Pearson
  (Henry Michelson)
The Coat Room at the Chesterfield
  (Frank Heller)
The Ample Room at the Mansfield
  (Isadore Dretzin)
The Jayne Mansfield Room at the Biltmore
  (Bob Criar)
The Engine Room at the Thunderbird
  (Si Wincelberg)
The Grit Room at the Sands
  (George L. Fischer)
The Room for Improvement—at any hotel
  (Ralph Bloomfield)

And to verify the need for this creative thinking, Carrie
Greer sent along a clipping from the *Omaha World Herald*
stating: "Construction on urgently needed hotels can't start
until somebody thinks up some more cute names for cocktail
lounges." Hotel men: Please proceed.

The rash of Hilton Hotel jokes has invited endless and
fruitless variations. The originals were: In Pisa, they're building the Tiltin' Hilton; in Moscow, the Comrade Hilton; in
Berlin, the Heil Hilton.

The new crop includes:

In Reno	The Jiltin' Hilton
In Arizona	The Wiltin' Hilton
For archeologists	The Piltdown Hilton

For cheese lovers   The Stilton Hilton
For the over-spent   The Up-to-the Hilton

When Doug Andrews, who handles publicity for Doubleday, began mulling over the firm's spy novel *It Can't Always
Be Caviar,* by Johannes Simmel, the first spy story ever to incorporate recipes for delectable food, he hit on the idea of
soliciting dishes appropriate for spy stories from the editorial
staff.

He should have known better. Among the offerings which
came in were:

From Louise Thomas:
    Cop Suey
    Stooled Pigeon
    Riot Squab
    Murderer's Roe
    Raisin Bail
    Jugged Rabbit
    Thyme Bomb
    Grilled Chicken
    Death House Cookies

From Louise Chastain:
    Borscht Karloff
    Hamburglar
    Thicken Plot Pie
    Mobster Thermidor
    Drown 'n Serve Rolls
    Cadavriar
    Waterfelon

From Marie Reno:
    Stoolpigeon Pie
    Roast Turnkey
    Chocolate Noose
    Ginger Wail

From Ruth Fell:
    Monster Cheese
    High Scream Soda
    Hot Battered Biscuits
    Eggs Benzedrine
    Peasant Under Glass
    Beef Strontium
    Stiletto and tomato salad
    Molotov cocktail
    Scrambled Yeggs
    Pistol Whip
    Club Sandwich
    Poisonberry Pie
    Peas and karates
    Wilde bore and brain squash

From R. W. Daugherty:
    Oysters on the Half Skull
    Crime de Menthe on the Rock
    Bier
    Veal cutthroat
    Roguefort Dressing
    Decapi-taters
    Hari Karotts
    Stole House Cookies

From Larry Ashmead:
    Arty-chokes
    Aspic in the Back
    Axe fines herbes

From Angela Pozzi:
    Safe crackers with cheese
    Broiled live mobster
    Cooked goose

Other suggestions included strangled eggs, beaten biscuits,

chicken croakettes, hangman's mousse, and rabbit's punch, to say nothing of mints' spy and punk-in-pie.

Of course, the rest of the country was in no mood to let this pass by. Other contributors bounded to the forefront with:

From Mary Duclos:
    Chili con carnage
    Baby Ruthless candy
    Police catch-up

From Derek and Elvira Brigg:
    Broken Neck Clams
    Scram Chowder
    Soup de Jury
    Lamb Cops
    Jujitsuey
    Chateau Brigand
    Frankfurtives
    Dead Beets
    Drowned Betty
    Rape Suzettes
    Mess of plottage

From Priscilla Rothschild:
    Police custardy
    Arrest con pollo
    Assaulted nuts

And Marie Morton aptly seals the whole bloody mess off by reminding everyone of a fine old adage: Too many crooks spoil the broth.

Of course, you can go on about cooks and cooking forever. For instance, Paul Thead feels that holidays should be brightened with special dishes: For a starter, there are Prankfurters for Halloween.

And then there is the entire list of Unlikely Cook Books to contend with:

The How to Carve Cookbook	for surgeons
The Viennese Torts Cookbook	for lawyers
The Salad Days Cookbook	for teen-agers
The Rook Cookbook	for chess players

And dogs have preoccupied author Richard Gardner so much that he completed an entire book for Doubleday called *The Secret of Cooking for Dogs*. One of his special delicacies: Tripe Delight Fantastic.

As a brimming glass of bicarbonate to correct any literary indigestion from the above menu, we offer an uncertified story from Jeffrey, who claims that a man who worked as a human cannon ball told the circus manager that he was about to retire after years of service on the job.

The manager wouldn't hear of it. "You *can't* retire," he said. "Where else could I find a man of your calibre?"

GAMES FOR CHAPTER TEN

You can consider this chapter as a rest cure. The games are simple, brief, and easy.

UNLIKELY COCKTAIL ROOMS

How many of these can you create? Example: The Bottoms-up Room at the Breakers, the Cracker Room at the Ritz?

Excellent	12
Good	8
Fair	4

TILTIN' HILTON

If the hotel in Pisa, Italy is the Tiltin' Hilton, how many others of this sort can you whip together?

Excellent	3
Good	2
Fair	1

MOBSTER THERMIDOR

You have been assigned the job of making up a menu for the local jail. Among the dishes you've inherited for this job are cop suey, hamburglar, and mints' spy. How many others of these culinary delights can you create?

Excellent	20
Good	10
Fair	5

chapter eleven

THE OLD SWITCHEROO

Note to Game Maniacs:

The game section here is a bit thin, and probably best fits in to Group Noodling in your living room rather than when you are alone in bed, where Night Terrors might strike. However, if you care to chance it, turn to page 149 and have a go.

Some time ago, I received a clipping from E. H. Ketchledge of the New York State College of Forestry, snipped from the "Proceedings of the Lockwood Conference on Suburban Forest and Ecology, Bulletin 652." On page 34, the text reads:

"Longfellow first used the term 'forest primeval.' His conception was of an inhabited Acadia, not a virgin forest, where the hand of man has never set foot."

Unintentionally, the author of this twisted metaphor was indulging in the old game of the Switcheroo, which has caused more groans throughout this land than the Income Tax Bureau.

No one will be able to discover just where the Switcheroo started, and very few are likely to want to find out. Probably one of the hoariest of the lot is the story of the native king who hoarded so many thrones in the attic of his straw hut that it finally collapsed. The moral to the story, of course, is: People who live in grass houses shouldn't stow thrones.

The form of the Switcheroo varies considerably from time to time, but most of them seem to rely on some utterly ridiculous kind of fairy tale, painfully contrived in the most elaborate way in order to set up the gag. Actually, the Switcheroo would not be so bad if the long-winded story-teller didn't take such a long time in his initial set up. That the shorter the set up, the better the gag is almost axiomatic; but few hardy chroniclers recall this rule when it comes to the Switcheroo.

William Kriebel did it admirably when he dropped me a line about the man who threw his wallet into a pool of fish, who grabbed it and tossed it back and forth like a basketball.

"It was a case of carp-to-carp walleting," says Mr. Kriebel.

With that as a starter, you are now warned about those Switcheroos which are to follow, and from now on in, you read at your own risk.

From Cole Pilcher:
> The Persian fleet at Salamis got so jittery waiting for the expected Athenian attack that they passed the word around: Beware of skiffs bearing Greeks.

From Dick Sears:
> A New England textile plant lost a considerable amount of inventory during a recent flood. The reason: Too many brooks spoil the cloth.

From Homer Overly:
> The tower radioed a pilot that he had a hole in the bottom of his gas tank, and that he was to fly upside down to prevent it from spilling. "Loop before you leak," was the message.

From Henna Arond Zacks:
> In Tibet, a yak accidentally wandered into a deep pit where rubble was being burned. Within moments, a native discovered the tragedy and yelled: "Oh, my baking yak!"

From Trudy Drucker:
> A manufacturer has built a new type of track shoe with

both a clock and pedometer. They will be known as "the soles which time men's tries."

From George P. Schmidt:

A biologist boasted of changing the behavior patterns of rodents. Reason: He was pulling habits out of rats.

Also: A scientist during the Depression found a job skinning eels in a Government lab. Reason: He was contributing to the Nude Eel.

From Ed Horr:

A horse farm made it a habit to bottle-feed its young colts when they were only a few days old. Reason: A foal and his mummy are soon parted.

Also: A botanist working on some plants found a new bug on them, and thereby took a new lice on leaf.

From Ralph Henry:

An espionage chief urged his staff to cut down on long, expensive telegrams and cables. His order: "Don't wire until you see the flights of their spies."

Also from Henna Arond Zacks:

A top executive tried to prevent gall stones by rolling down hill. Reason: A rolling boss gathers no stones.

Also: A cow in the pasture found she had to excuse anything her favorite bull did. Reason: To err is human, to forgive, bovine.

From William Olmstead:

A GI returned from Germany with an antique beer mug. To keep it safe, he put it in a special recess in his grandfather's clock, where it miraculously escaped harm in an earthquake. Reason: A niche in time saves stein.

From Allan Bosworth:

The father of quintuplets received so many hundreds of congratulatory telegrams that he was forced to say: "I seem to have sold my birthrate for a pot of messages."

From Dorothy Larson:

A young Indian left his reservation to study electricity. He later returned to his people and found that the large community bathroom had no electricity. He immediately installed a lighting system, thus becoming the first Indian to wire a head for a reservation.

From Harry Ober:

A man was concerned over whether his new electric tooth brush would injure the enamel on his teeth. His worries were unfounded when he discovered that the tooth is stronger than friction.

From Brad Boynton:

During an international basketball tournament, those countries with very tall players were running away with the tournament. Said a spectator: Many lands make height work.

From Theodore Schwarz, Jr.:

An umpire, hated by everyone and brutal enough to beat his wife, finally decided to reform. He asked his little boy to sit on his lap. The boy refused. Reason: The son never sets on the brutish umpire.

From *Chilton, Wisc., Times* via Reverend William Zimmer:

A king ordered the heads of several of his counts chopped off because they refused to reveal where they buried their treasures. As the axes began falling, one count decided to change his mind and spill the secret—but too late. Moral: Don't hatchet your counts before they chicken. Also: One pregnant Indian wife slept on a hide of elk; another on buffalo; a third on hippopotamus skin. The first and second each had a son, the third had twin boys. Moral: The squaw of the hippopotamus is equal to the sons of the squaws on the other two hides.

From Don Quinn:
An East Indian potentate couldn't handle the giant herds of wild elephants which attacked his palace, so he cleared out as fast as he could, leaving a sign: REIGN CALLED ON ACCOUNT OF GAME.

From William Osborn:
A kind zoo keeper kept his lion house warm by using the hair shed by the lion's mane, for insulation. Result: A case of denning the lion in his beard.

From Jean Jeffries:
During a summer of chilly and erratic weather, the owners of a chain of swimming pools found that they could people some of the pools all of the time, and all of the pools some of the time, but they could not people all of the pools all of the time.

From Gerald Raftery:
Aldous Huxley once wrote a novel about the lecherous Spaniard who used to go to the beach to leer at the girls in bikinis. Title: *After Many a Swimmer Sighs the Don.*

With this, we can draw this brief and unwholesome chapter to a merciful close. If it should leave you speechless, you may find comfort in the story Jerry Wald tells about Gabriele d'Annunzio, the Italian poet, who was invited to come to Hollywood to write scripts. D'Annunzio declined on the basis that there would be no one to talk to. When he was assured that the best interpreters would be provided, he said: "With whom would the interpreters talk?"

GAMES FOR CHAPTER ELEVEN

This is Make-Up-a-Story time, and it involves the very simple procedure of taking the following statements, twisting them into a horrible, reversal sort of pun, and then making up a story to justify it. For instance, take the old saying: "People in glass houses shouldn't throw stones."

You can approximate this noble proverb, and murder it at the same time, by changing it to: People in grass houses shouldn't stow thrones.

Then it becomes only a matter of making a ridiculous story up to go with it. In this case, the classic story is about a native king who hoards thrones in the attic of his straw hut, until it finally collapses. The twisted proverb is thus justified, your friends are thus completely alienated, and you'll have plenty of time to yourself to do the rest of the games in this book.

For the first portion, we'll make it easy for you, and give you a twisted proverb. Simply make up a story to go with:

(1) Beware of skiffs bearing Greeks.
(2) Too many brooks spoil the cloth.
(3) Oh, my baking yak!

Now take the following statements, twist them, and make up a story in addition:

(1) These are the times which try men's souls.
(2) A fool and his money are soon parted.
(3) Take a new lease on life.
(4) Don't fire until you see the whites of their eyes.

(5) A rolling stone gathers no moss.

(6) To err is human, to forgive, divine.

(7) A stitch in time saves nine.

(8) I have sold my birthright for a mess of pottage.

(9) Truth is stranger than fiction.

(10) Many hands make light work.

(11) The sun never sets on the British empire.

(12) Don't count your chickens before they hatch.

(13) Game called on account of rain.

(14) The square of the hypotenuse is equal to the sum of the squares of the other two sides.

As a bonus, and for additional torture, you might take as many proverbs as you can recall, and list them with opposite meanings.

Example:

Too many cooks spoil the broth.

Many hands make light work.

May the leaves of the fig trees bring you shade, sustenance, and comfort.

chapter twelve

THREE QUARTERS OF A TON OF SODA BISCUITS, OR: THE QUICK BROWN FOX JUMPS THE GUN

Note to Game Maniacs:

Officially, I suppose you could say that there isn't a game section here. It's more of a nightmare, a true story of a hideous, frightening mistake in the Game of Life, than which nothing is whicher. Of course, though, the whole chapter is really a game, and more people than I care to think about have already joined in to take a crack at it. Perhaps you would, too. Especially if you'd like to get rid of your guests.

It was a day, like any other day.

A Met outfielder dropped his pen three times before he could sign his contract. A stranger in New York stopped a hip-looking bopster and asked him how he could get to Carnegie Hall. The reply: "Practice, man. Practice!" A yes-man in Hollywood told his producer: "You can't prove nodding by me." A TRADE WINDS reader by the actual name of Steve Brody dropped me a line that he heard that an actor turned down a role in *Lassie* because it was a bit part. Another reader named Morton Marcus wrote to say he heard an unreliable report that a script for another canine star was turned down by the dog's manager because it had the title *Tin Foiled Again.*

But all this was inconsequential.

Most of the trouble was buried in an innocent-looking letter postmarked Cleveland, Ohio:

"Dear John G. Fuller:

'The quick brown fox jumped over the good lazy rabbits.' I think that is right. Now, my question is, has anyone come up with a good English sentence (or even a not-so-good English sentence) which uses fewer than the forty-four letters of this sentence, containing every letter of the alphabet. It seems I have read one somewhere, but I cannot recall for certain. It would probably make a good, but likely frustrating, pastime or party game.

"I ask *you* because I have no intention of wasting *my* time with this foolishness."

(Signed)
Dale Betcher

I wrote back promptly:

"Dear Dale Betcher: That's a real challenge. Let's see if we can find somebody to try it. I think it's 'over the lazy dog,' rather than rabbits, but who cares. Let's try."

Mr. Betcher wrote back promptly:

"Thanks for the correction. It comes back to me now. Well, in my mind, Mr. Fuller, you have not, by your correction of me, made impossible the search for an English sentence containing every letter of the alphabet with fewer letters than 'The quick brown fox . . .' Your correction of my sentence has but thirty-five letters; simply by changing the second *the* to *a*, the sentence is reduced to thirty-three letters, which is only a few letters away from the perhaps impossible ultimate: A twenty-six letter sentence containing all twenty-six letters of the alphabet.

"The quick brown fox will probably never be replaced as a typewriter key-tester even by a shorter sentence, but such a sentence may be thought of by someone and I certainly would be interested in seeing, as you wrote, if we can find somebody to try it. Thanks for your reply and my best to you."

Never in the history of the United States Mail has there been a more innocent exchange of letters.

I put the letter on the shelf for several weeks, until I had the right amount of space to fill in TRADE WINDS, and then wrote:

"We've just heard from Dale Betcher, of Cleveland, Ohio, who is completely fed up with the classical typewriting test sentence: 'The quick brown fox jumps over the lazy dog.' Mr. Betcher wants to know why we have to remain satisfied with this old turkey, and why we can't find another test sentence that would contain every letter of the alphabet, without repeating any of the letters. This is a challenge to try men's souls."

Everything would have been all right if I had let it go on that. But the next day, Jim Fixx, feature editor of the *Saturday Review* called.

"We're just seven lines short on the column for this week," he said. "Can you give me a fill?"

I got out the typewriter, looked at the copy, and figured that it might be better to give a little enticement to readers who might not care to accept his challenge of a new type-test sentence. I tried to think of the most unlikely award for such efforts, and for no reason at all settled on soda biscuits. I hadn't heard them spoken of since my grandmother had caught me stealing from the cookie jar, but I was sure I could run down to the corner grocer and buy a few packages if one or two readers were able to come up with such a difficult assignment. So I added to the copy:

". . . but on behalf of Mr. Betcher we are willing to offer ten pounds of soda biscuits to anyone who can come up with another sentence containing all the letters of the alphabet, and not more than ten letters longer than 'The quick brown fox.'"

Just why I became so generous as to permit *more* letters than the original sentence, I'll never know. And why I didn't qualify the offer and confine it to the first five respondents is another item that should be checked by a competent alienist.

However, the column went to press, and I took off for the quiet of Martha's Vineyard island on what I laughingly thought was a well-earned vacation. I never gave the column another thought.

Until several days later, that is. When the phone rang, it was my secretary.

"They just backed a mail truck up to the door," she said.

"Oh?"

"And dropped off a few sacks of mail."

"Oh? Why am I getting so popular?"

"It's not you," she said. "It's the Quick Brown Fox. He's come home to roost. Or whatever foxes do."

"Ouch," I said, not without a quiver.

"I figure roughly," Miss Martin said, "that you owe something like half of a maximum-load box car. At this reading."

"I see," I said, trying to picture a large, red box car.

"I've already written a form postcard to send out. Would you like to hear it?"

"Why not?"

"Dear So and So: I have just notified Mr. Fuller, who is on vacation, about your solution to the problem and he is coming back at the end of the month with the finest soda biscuits available for you."

"That's very friendly," I said.

"I think so, too," said Miss Martin. "We'll need more postcards."

"The least of my worries," I said.

"I'd better run now. I think I hear another truck," Miss Martin said.

"Yes," I said. "Don't keep them waiting."

"Have a nice vacation."

"Sure."

"Bye."

"Bye."

I hung up and went into the living room. My wife, who is English, had a cup of tea on the coffee table.

"Would you like a biscuit with it?" she said.

By the time the end of summer rolled around, I was able to report the following in TRADE WINDS:

A BISCUIT, AS DESCRIBED BY *Webster's New Collegiate Dictionary*, is a kind of unleavened bread, plain, sweet, or fancy, formed into flat cakes and baked hard. A soda biscuit, according to the same source, is leavened with sodium bicarbonate and sour milk, or buttermilk—certainly not too attractive a prospect when you think it over. The word soda is said to be derived from the Arabic *suda* meaning "splitting headache."

In a wild state of generosity in this column several weeks ago, we were rash enough to offer ten pounds of soda biscuits to anyone who could supply a new sentence to replace the tired and dog-eared typing exercise "The quick brown fox . . ."

Never let it be said that the readers of TRADE WINDS are slow to take up a challenge.

Our latest calculations indicate that we are now in the soup for approximately three-quarters of a ton of soda biscuits, a fact that provides a rare, personal insight into why the Arabs link the whole thing with splitting headaches. We hasten to add that the contest is now closed.

Because of our solemn obligation to TW readers, we are leaving no biscuit unturned to supply the etymological athletes who responded so heroically, with their just reward.

But you don't simply walk to the nearest corner grocery store, as we thought we might, and ask the clerk to wrap up three-quarters of a ton of soda biscuits. In fact, one wholesale baker, in responding to our query said, "What are you—some kind of a nut or something?" and promptly hung up. Another suggested that soda biscuits went out when the flanged wheel came in. A third made some generally uncomplimentary remarks and asked us to hold out until Mental Health Week rolled around. From national bakeries, we were able to elicit genuine concern and considerable sympathy, only to learn that there is no such thing as soda biscuits, *per se*, on the open market today. What's more, we've learned, the whole biscuit-cracker-cookie hierarchy is fraught with dangerous lexical disturbances, pitting brother against brother, executive against executive. No one, it seems, can decide just what *is* a biscuit compared to a cookie or a cracker. One of the largest biscuit companies in the nation was forced to admit that it didn't make biscuits—it made only crackers or cookies.

We are now in the process of working out secret negotiations with one of the country's leading bakers to provide the winners with a full measure of ambrosia. By the time our next fortnightly column rolls around, we'll report on this in full. In the meantime, let's examine a sampling of some of the results.

It can only be a sampling. A gentleman by the name of Ellsworth Geist, for instance, has come up with sixty-seven sentences containing each letter of the alphabet, including one that reads: "Overjoyed pix king thawed by cozy film queens." Roger F. Williams sends: "By jove, my quick study of lexicography won a prize." And it will.

G. M. Ostrander brings in current Hollywood gossip with: " 'Dick,' quoth Liz, 'beware of sexy, vamping jades.' " Herbert Harvey has arranged a commentary on the television scene with: "Quiz show vexed by lack of rating jump."

Photographer Ivan Dmitri has taken time out from his tripod long enough to put together the thirsty sentence: "Hey, Jack, I'm frozen. Mix up, chill, and serve a big quart—wow!" He goes on to say: "This story suggests that there may be something in the offing more exciting, more delectable even, than the accomplishment of eighty words per minute."

No self-respecting psychoanalyst can ignore sex, and Dr. Mason Rose of Hollywood keeps up the tradition with his sentence: "Sexy zebras just prowl and vie for quick, hot matings." He adds: "This should lend zest to learning the keyboard."

But there are others. Chuck Haydon suggests: "The quixotic

women find love's zest by joyous parking." And Betty Barn-
dollar joins the chorus with: "Many-wived Jack laughs at
probe of sex quiz."

TRADE WINDS and the *Saturday Review* come in for a
share of attention with: "Saturday Review magazine quips by
far excel the jokes," (Pauline Engel), and "J. G. Fuller, by
hacked wit and moxie, quiets zippy nerves." (Stan Wenner).

Mrs. Roger Blanchard signs her entry "Alex Z. Waverly Q.
Buckingham Stopford, Jr.," and closes with the notation that
she'll settle for five pounds of soda biscuits and a quart jug
of vodka.

She is not alone. Joseph Fagan asks for his soda biscuits
soaked in scotch; Don Kanabay would like us to throw in a
couple of cans of soup; Cecil Goff protests that he's on a diet;
David Adler would have us send the biscuits to his mother-in-
law; Mac Teplitz wonders if he could get peanut butter, too;
Charles Olasky, Captain, U. S. Navy, Retired, would prefer
hardtack or sea biscuits; Mrs. Herbert Browarsky would rather
have a left-handed moustache cup with matching saucer; and
C. D. Firestone concludes his note: "By the way, what *is* a
soda biscuit?"

We regret to announce that some TW readers are sneaky.
Lilyn Carlton supplies the sentence: "Baby knows all his letters except: d, f, g, j, m, q, u, v, and z." Then she adds:
" 'Quick, man! The X-ray!' cried Dr. G. J. Bloomps to Dr.
V. W. Zof." And, in addition, she joins several other below-
the-belt biscuit winners with: "The quick brown *dog* jumps
over the lazy *fox*."

Many readers supplied a sentence that turns out to be an
old standard: "Pack my box with five dozen liquor jugs." They
will receive token awards, not quite as much as those for original contributions, but just as tasty.

Not long after this, I was able to report in the column:

We are now prepared to set to rest officially the soda biscuit
crisis, resulting from our rash offer to readers who could
supply a substitute sentence to replace "The quick brown

fox . . ." Feeling that no product would be too good for the contestants, if that is what you would call them, the Arnold Bakers, of Greenwich, Connecticut, have been kind enough to put together spanking fresh packages of old-fashioned cookies in half a dozen gourmet flavors, and to ship them off via parcel post to our hungry wordsmiths. Such an assortment will not only put to shame the soda biscuits that we originally promised, but will indeed be a feast fit for Olympus.

Late entries for the contest brought a response from E. A. Heath, of Evanston, Illinois, who was easily bored with the challenge of putting together a sentence with each letter of the alphabet in it. He came up with several sentences using each letter *twice*, among them being: "A plump wench flagged a Zanzibar kayak to query a vivid chief squaw about juju maxixes." And that's not all. Imposing the limitation of metric feet, rhyme, and the limerick form, Mr. Heath came through with no less than six limericks, some of them including a *triple* use of each letter. Among them:

> When an expert burlesque queen named Maizy
> Stripping velvet, became very lazy
> She would quickly exhibit
> Just one jeweled explicit
> Gliding off from the jokesters like crazy.

After the soda biscuit crisis had died down, another letter from Mr. Dale Betcher, the perpetrator of the whole thing, came along, I was a little afraid to open it. But I did, and it read:

Dear John G. Fuller:

I have read your recent column. You have quite a problem. I am a little sorry for you, and for *your* sake, I wish I had never started this whole thing. But my sympathy for you is limited. After all, you made it too easy. You should have asked for *fewer* letters. I am coming to New York in a few days, but, believe me, not to help you solve your present problems. Soda biscuits? Good grief, as Charlie Brown is always saying.

In all seriousness, though, your readers came through with some good sentences. I hope *you* manage to let them take home the bacon—er, biscuits.

Echoes, however, kept coming in for months afterward. Susan Strasser wrote that they're even doing it in France. When she opened her new Hermes typewriter, she found two examples on the *essai d'écriture*:

"Zoe, ma grande fille, veut que je boive ce whisky dont je ne veux pas."

And: "Monsieur Jack, vous dactlylographiez bien mieux que votre ami Wholf."

Said Miss Strasser: "*I* think they're better."

Alan Beerbower, however, summed up the whole incident for us admirably:

The quick brown fox has jumped and gone
The empty liquor jugs remain;
But still the pangrams jingle on
Like clinkers from the fevered brain.

And indeed they do. I walked by the Olivetti Underwood typewriter company on Fifth Avenue, where a sidewalk typewriter is available for any passer-by to test. The company carefully preserves these *graffiti* in a file—but only rarely does "The quick brown fox . . ." appear.

Instead, we found some other morsels, which are reproduced below with faithful accuracy:

HOWIE—WHERE ARE YOU? EXCELSIOR, YOU FATHEAD!!! THIS IS NO NIGHT TO BE OUT WITHOUT AN UMBRELLA

my daddy ate three dinners his name is tubby

Look at me, I can type/ almost

Please help me, I8ve been eaten by a typewriter

Elizabeth Taylor should marry Norman Mailer if note a sailor.

I am a psychotic, withdrawn from the world, but what the hell at least I'm not noticing the problems of reality

Beethove received a rousing ovation upon the performing of his immaral nineth symphony . . .

YOU ARE A FINK FOR READING THIS

This is ridiculous when you think about it, I mean standing in the street and typeing, for gosh sakes

But no more ridiculous, I might add, than the quick brown fox and two and a half tons (final count) of ersatz soda biscuits.

Because of so many requests to record for history the results of The Great Soda Biscuit Fiasco, we list herewith part of the sentences received, whether they exactly qualify or not:

From Marshall Kuhn:
GROUND FLAPJACKS QUIVER THE BUSY WAX MAZE.

From Francis X. de Javanne:
XAVIER PICKED BRIGHT YELLOW JONQUILS FOR MITZI.

From William Kite:
QUICK WAXY BUGS JUMP THE FROZEN VELDT.

From Mrs. Arthur Damick:
ELIZA QUICKLY MIXED THE VERY BIG JAR OF SAP.

From Alma L. Egerer:
JUMPY ZEBRAS FEINT WHILE QUICK DOGS VEX.
MIGHTY PIQUED ZEBRAS FLICK VIXEN JOWLS.
NEW PAROXYSMS BAFFLED QUICK FIGHTERS VIA JAZZ.
BIG QUARTZ BOXES HOLD MY VERY FINE PEWTER JACKS.
A GROUP OF SIX VITAL BONY CHICKS SQUIRMED WITH LAZY
    JOY.
MY CRAZY FOX WHELPS QUIT VOICING BAD JOKES.

LAX DOZY BUCKS QUIT REST AND JUMPED FORTH VEERING WEST.

PROUD JUST MEN FIGHT BOLD QUACKERY WITH VEXED ZEAL.

From L. A. "Pete" Morrow:

RAZE FIVE NEW BIG JUXTAPOSED HOMES QUICKLY.

CLIQUES FOR GAZEBOS WITH BRICK MOVE UP AND DEFY JINX.

FIXED JAVELINS WHISPERING QUIETLY ZOOM BACK.

JUDGE VOWS SPECK IS BARQUE OF ZANTHOXYLUM.

I KNOW BRIGHT JADE QUETZALS FLY UP OVER MEXICO.

A GLAZED BUT QUIET WIFELY LOOK CAN JAR THE SEXY VAMP.

From E. Derby:

VEXED, PAW IS JERKING THE QUILT OFF MY COZY BED.

From David Adler:

SQUDGY FEX, BLANK JIMP CRWTH VOX!

From Irving N. Fisher:

TWO JOYFUL VIXENS SQUIRT MILK UPON THE CAGED ZEBRA.

From Barbara Bromer:

QUIXOTIC KNIGHTS' WIVES ARE FOUND ON JUMPY OLD ZEBRAS.

WITH MY ZAX I FIGHT AND QUELL A PACK OF KNAVISH JIBERS.

FROM QUIET ZYGOTES WAX VIABLE HENS AND JACKANAPES.

"QUIZ PROBLEMS VEX AND FRIGHTEN ME," YAWNED JACK.

From Dr. Alvan R. Feinstein:

AX OF MIGHTY SQUAW JOLTS DOZEN BLACK VIPERS.

XYLOPHONE WIZARD BEGETS QUICK JIVE FORM.

SPHYNX QUITS FLOCK: VIZOR JAMS WRONG BED.

ZEPHYR BLOWS QUACK VIXEN TO JUDGE'S FARM.

From Doris B. Garey:

MAN VEXED BY COLD GALE KNOWS JOY OF THE QUIET ZEPHYR.

From Mrs. Charles Reinwald:

WE DISLIKE TO EXCHANGE JOB LOTS OF SIZES VARYING FROM A QUARTER UP.

PROBABLY MY OXEN WILL HAUL A DOZEN LOADS OF GRAVEL JUST AS QUICKLY.

THE JOB REQUIRES EXTRA PLUCK AND ZEAL FROM EVERY YOUNG WAGE EARNER.

WHENEVER THE BLACK FOX JUMPED THE SQUIRREL GAZED VERY SUSPICIOUSLY.

From Don Kanabay:

A QUIET JAY MIGHT FLY BACKWARDS OVER A NAZI PX.

From Mark Ryder:

A VEXING QUIZ COWED BOTH OF MY JERKY PALS.

WAX JOCKEYS QUIZ VAMP'S BLIGHTED FERN.

THE BLACK QUARTZ LYNX WAS A JIVY IMP OF GOD.

FIVE JOES MIGHT BOX A DOZEN WRAPS QUICKLY.

From Richard D. Kahoe:

J. Q. GELB AND V. W. PHIZ STRUCK MY FOX.

From Bill Toedt:

MY CONGRATULATIONS FOR THE QUICK WORKING FINISHED BIZARRE X-RAY INVENTION.

From Virgil J. Vogel:

FOUR JOVIAL KAZAKS IN QUEST OF YAKS CAMPED BETWIXT TWO BIG HILLS.

VEXED NAZIS PERSECUTE A GOOD MANY JEWS WHO DON'T QUICKLY OBEY ADOLF HITLER.

ABDICATION OF KING ZOG IS EXPECTED VERY QUICKLY AFTER HIS JUNE WEDDING MARCH.

PROVEN JOY CAN BE GOTTEN FROM QUITE AN EXHILARATING WALK BESIDE AZURE WATERS.

FIVE THICKETS OF QUAKING ASPEN, BOX ELDER, AND JUNE-BERRY LINED THE FROZEN SWAMP.

From Genurine Ball:

ONE DUCK QUACKED BRAVELY: FOR PURSUING HIM WAS A MEXICAN JAZZ COMBO.

From Bob Allenson:

WILLIAM JEX QUICKLY BOUGHT FIVE DOZEN REPUBLICANS.

From Erich A. Von Fange:

SCHIZOPHRENIC LAMB VOWS TO GO FIX QUEER JADED TURKEY.

LAZY CRAFTY MIDWIVES QUIP BY JUKEBOX HANGOUT.

FIVE OLD QUETZALS WAX ANGRY AT A HUMPBACKED JAY.

SPRINKLE FIVE QUARTS OF MY JADE WAX ON ZEBRA FOR COUGH.

From Jean Challman:

JACKDAWS CHASE LYNX FROM QUIVERING PET ZEBRAS.

From Charles Petrie, Jr.:

WHILE AT PILING BOXES OF ZINC, I JUMPED VERY QUICKLY.

From Cecil W. Goff:

MAKING BREEZY QUOTES HELPED VEX JACK FAW.

From J. C. Brown:

HE KEPT VEXING ME WITH FRANTIC JOURNEYS HIDDEN BY QUIET ZEAL.

From Julian and Eric Ross:

QUITE A FEW VERY PROMINENT ZULUS JUST CAN'T GET VERY EXCITED ABOUT HACKENSACK.

SEVEN WILDLY PANTING FRUITFLIES GAZED ANXIOUSLY AT THE JUICY BOUNDING KUMQUAT.

A PRELIMINARY EXAM BY A QUALIFIED VET SHOWS THAT THE MAJOR REASON WHY THE DOG DOZES IS THAT HE IS A SACKHOUND.

A POX ON YOU, JERGENS, OLD BEANBAG, YOU'VE SQUASHED MY FAVORITE ZWEIBACK.

From W. D. Merritt, Jr.:

JOHN QUICKLY EXTEMPORIZED FIVE TOW BAGS.

From Mary Rosa:

A BIG JEEP MOVES QUICKLY WHEN EXERCISED OFTEN.

From Keith Monroe:

SYMPATHIZING WOULD FIX QUAKER OBJECTIVES.

PROVABLE MARK WILL JUSTIFY EXCHANGED QUIZ.

From Maristan Chapman:

A FIRM QUIZZING UPSET THE EXCITED, JEALOUS AND OVER-
WORKED BODYGUARD.

THE PUBLIC WAS AMAZED TO VIEW THE QUICKNESS AND DEX-
TERITY OF THE JUGGLER.

MY HELP SQUEEZED IN AND JOINED THE WEAVER AGAIN BE-
FORE SIX O'CLOCK.

WE QUICKLY SEIZED THE BACK AXLE AND JUST SAVED
IT FROM GOING PAST HIM.

THE FAMOUS XYLOGRAPHER QUICKLY MADE A VERY NEAT
AZURE JEWEL BOX.

From Marjorie F. Johnson:

SIX PLUMP BOYS GUZZLED CHEAP RAW VODKA QUITE JOY-
FULLY.

FIVE SICK ZEBRAS MIXED UP QUINCE JELLY WITH EGGNOG.

TWO QUESTIONS OF CAPSIZING TAXED BRAVE JACK MIGHTILY.

WHY DO VERY JEALOUS BOYS SQUEEZE EXTRA FICKLE GIRLS?

THE GIFT BOX OF JIGSAW PUZZLES QUICKLY DROVE ME
NUTS.

From Robert Strawn:

ARE MR. M. Q. VEAZY'S OLD JOKES AND BOX SPRINGS WORTHY
OF OUR CONVERSATION?

THE CHANCELLOR OF THE EXCHEQUER EMBEZZLED JUNK
FROM GYPSIES WITH VIGOR.

THE QUICK WAVE EXCHANGED MY JUKE BOX TOP FOR OLD
RAZORS.

From Etta M. Nelson:

JIFFY QUIZ PROGRAMS ON TV BALK EXCITED WATCHERS.

FAIRYLIKE ZEPHYRS WOVE QUIXOTIC MUSIC ON GOLD BAN-
JOS.

From Ruth N. McCready:

EXAMPLES OF URBAN RENEWAL HAVE QUICKLY JEOPARDIZED
YESTERDAY'S GRAY TENEMENTS.

From Mildred B. Buhler:

LAZY JOB PICKED FIVE OR SIX TOUGH WARM QUINCES.
WE SIMPLY CHOSE TO QUIT VYING FOR EXTRA KEEN ADZ JOBS.
HE QUICKLY WAVED FOR SIX EMPTY ZINC BEER JUGS.

From Doug Wylie:

THE QUIXOTIC ZEBRA KEPT VIEWY DAMSEL GOLFERS UN-
JAPED.

From Tom Morton:

HEY
    BLOW FAST DARK JAZZ
        PICTURESQUE MAGNAVOX!

From James Unger:

FIVE CRAZY CLOWNS JUMPED QUICKLY INTO THE BIG BOX.

From Harold Grunewald:

QUICKLY ZELDA WOVE EIGHT NUBBY FLAX JUMPERS.

From Ann Brunk:

JACK'S QUIET WAXED FLOORS HAVE MANY PUZZLING KNOBS.

From C. Gevers:

A BAND OF JOKERS WITH SMALLPOX QUIT GAZA FOR VICHY.
FIVE DOZEN BIG JERKS MAKE QUICK PLAYS FOR WHITE SOX.
VERY FEW ZANIES MADE A QUICK JOB OF SPELLING
XANTHOUS.

From Betty Scott:

A QUIXOTIC FEW MAY GIVE ZEBRA JOKES TO DOLPHINS.

From Joseph L. Eisendrath:

CAMPUS TV QUIZ: JUST WHY IS GOLD BURIED AT FORT KNOX?

From Donna Isaly:
UNDER A FOG COVER I SAW WITH QUALM OF JOY A PINK WAX ZEBRA.

From L. Jerome Stanton:
HOW QUICKLY DAFT JUMPING ZEBRAS VEX.

From Barb Landfield:
WAVES OF BAD EXOTIC JAZZ PIQUE THE KINGLY RAM.
BLACK RISQUE MOVIES PLAYS FAZE NOT THE WAX JUDGE.
WE GAVE HIM BLUFF QUIPS AND CRAZY EXIT JOKES.
FILMDOM'S JAZZ KING SQUINTS BACK OVER HIS WEEPY SAX.
THE QUEER JUDGE FELL IN THE VAST EMPTY ZWEIBACK BOX.

From Ted Heath:
JOVIAL BRAHMA COWS FREQUENTLY PUKE GRAZED FLAX.
JACK LOVED PIGMY ZUCCHINI SQUASH FIXED WITH CRABS.
MR. KEWJOY EXCELS AT GOLF, PINOCHLE AND EVEN BEZIQUE.
WE FIND BROOKLYN ZOO JAVA CHIMP CAGES QUITE SEXY.
IN JAPAN, A WIZARD FIXED EIGHTY BAROQUE BACK VOLUMES.

From Ruth H. Jacobs:
GOD GIVES THE GRAZING OX HIS MEAT
  HE QUICKLY HEARS THE SHEEP'S LOW CRY;
BUT MAN, WHO TAKES HIS FINEST WHEAT,
  SHOULD LIFT HIS JOYFUL PRAISES HIGH.
                                    (author unknown)

From Joanne Amstutz:
TWO QUACKS FORGO JAZZ ON MY VIVID BLUE XYLOPHONE.

From Edward M. Krauss:
JACK WILDE DID NOT GIVE MY BOX OF RIPE SQUASH TO THE ZOO.

From Dr. Jerry Litt:
MY VULGAR CAFE JUKE BOX THREW A DOZEN QUIPS.

From Patsy Felmet:
SIX POWERFUL ZOMBIS CAVORT AND JERK QUITE ROUGHLY.

From Marlow Sholander:
BRICK QUIZ WHANGS JUMPY VELDT FOX.
HEMP VOWS BLOCK FUGY QUARTZ JINX.

From Mr. and Mrs. Alan K. Borse:
KILLING QUIXOTIC FARMER BIZET PAVED JOHN'S WAY.
MY WIZARD FRAUGHT A QUICK POX ON A BEVY OF JEWELS.
BUZ FRIGHTENED MY LOVER, JACQUES, WITH A PICKAX.
BALZAC FOXED HARVEY, JACQUES' TWINKLY MAGPIE.
JOKING FRIGHT PIQUED WAXY BALZAC'S VENOM.

From Margaret Beidler:
THE ZEBRA KICKED OVER MY JUG OF EXQUISITE PLUM WINE.
THE VERY FUZZY BUG WAS STUCK, EXILED IN A QUINCE JAM
POT.
A BIG OX WAS STUCK IN A SIZZLING PUDDLE OF VERY HOT
QUINCE JAM.
ZOOKEEPERS DO EXPECT FEW QUAIL BUT HAVE MANY
JAGUARS.
ZIP OXYGEN QUICKLY BEFORE THE MAD WOMAN JABS HER
LIVER.

From Alan Kraus:
A MAN ON THE QUIZ SHOW EXPLODED A FAKE CIGAR, BY
JOVE!

From Suzanne Suskin:
A QUICK SHREWD GNOME PLAYS VEXING B FLAT JAZZ.

From D. L. Jacobus:
QUIT JAZZ; DEFY, VEX, WRECK, MANGLE PHOBIAS.

From Marlene Temaky:
THE JAGGED POX BRIEFLY STRUCK A WORM'S QUIVER ZONE.

From Gene Ellinger:
TAXI SQUIRMS BELOW JACKED-UP VAN IN HAZY BOG.

PRIZEFIGHT CHAMP BOXED DEVIL—NOW JUST SQUEAKS BY.
SIX KNAVES FROM QUOD JAB LAZY COP WITH GUN.
PITHY QUIZ SOLVER WON CAKE BOX FROM JUDGE.
LIZ, PIQUED ON JOB, GAVE MA FORTY AX WHACKS.

From G. W. Dueker:
ZERO GRAVITY OF SPACE MAY HEX A BAD NEW PROJECT
QUICKLY.

From Lewis S. Marks:
TV'S BIG QUIZ CHAMP DREW FOR LYNX JACKET.
MY VAIN WIFE LIKES HIGH PRICED QUARTZ BIJOUX.

From Alan Vaughan:
CRAZY QUIXOTE LOVED MOCK FIGHTS WITH PUNJABI.

From Alfred Basch:
BLACK WAXEN TAPERS QUIVERED AMAZINGLY JOYFUL LIGHT.
JUVENILES QUEST FOR GODLIKE CHAMPS OR BLOWZY DOXIES.
QUICKLY BLOW MEDITATIVE SAXOPHONE JAZZ FIGURES.

From W. Kendall Smith:
IF 3 BCD EQUALS XYZ THEN 5 JKL OVER 2 MPW GETS O
TO INCLUDE ALL THE NUMERALS JUST ADD THEM IN AS
IF 13   64   57   28   90

From Lawrence Levine:
ZYGODACTYL IBEX QUACK WHEN FEVER JUMPS.
HOT ZWEIBACK QUIETLY JINXES VAPID FROGMEN.

From John Munzer:
VAPID WOOZY MINX JERKS QUILT FROM FIG BRANCH.

From Betty Brout:
QUIZ: HOW DO I JUST PACK ALL OF MY VEXING TROUBLES
AWAY?
MY JEALOUS ZEBRA PICKED FIGHTS WITH A QUEER VIXEN.
ZOOMAN QUAVERED, "BADGER PUP IS JUST WEAKEST LYNX
OF THE CHAIN."

From Barbara Lewis:

> QUIVERING AND NUMB FOXY JACK WON ALL THE PRIZES.

From Renee Harris:

> A FAT ZEBRA, ON WAY TO EXHIBIT MOVED QUICKLY TO JOIN
> PIGS.

From: Dr. Joel Berger:

> WHY MINK RAVED BIG FOX QUIT LP JAZZ DISC.
> WHY SCAB MIKE RAVED FOX QUITTING JAZZ LP.

From John Mackenzie Cory:

> FEW QUITE LAZY MEN PICK HARD VEXING JOBS.

From Arlin H. Kaufman:

> WARY MAJOR QUENCHED BLAZING TRUCK OF EXPLOSIVES.

From John High:

> POPS QUICKLY JINXED GAMBLER WITH VIZOR.
> MINX WITH JODHPURS QUICKLY GAVE BIG FEZ.
> VET WON QUIZ JOB RHYMING POX AND FLOCKS.
> MAD PREXY WITH FEZ GAVE BACK JONQUILS.

From Mac Teplitz:

> XMAS HICK QUITS LAZY JOB OVER PAWING FIDO.

From G. Knight:

> HOWLING JUKE-BOX FANS DRIVE QUIET PAM CRAZY.

From James Herlihy:

> RICE, MAPS, JUNK, A FEZ AND A GLOVE BOX WERE ON THE
> QUAY.

From Roy C. Bates:

> ESP
> QUICKJUMPS
> THE FOGBOUND WALLS,
> VIZ., HEX-RAYS.
> ZEN-KUMQUAT-FED, VILE COPYRIGHT LAW X-PERTS JOB.
> A NORMAL CZECH JIG PIXY VOWS TO QUIT BAD FOLK MUSIC.

From R. J. Magee:

I QUIETLY GAVE UP BOOZE—SEND OFF CRACKER BOX WITH JAM.

FIVE JOLLY GNOMES PACKED A SQUARE BOX WITH ZIP.

From Annette Magee:

GUS JUST FINDS BUZZARD QUILLS TO MAKE VERY CHEAP WAX.

BRICK WAGONS HAVE JUST DUMPED SIXTY LOADS OF QUARTZ.

From Dianne J. Mahany:

FALLEN ARCHES HAVE JINXED A QUIET, GAWKY, MYOPIC ZEBRA.

A PUDGY QUIXOTIC ZEN BUDDHIST MADE HOT JAVA LIKE SWARF.

From John Olson:

FOUR QUIET BROWN OXEN JUMP OVER THE LAZY DUCK'S EGGS.

From Mondi Bridges:

A FILM ABOUT A JUG WINDS IN THE QUICK ZEPHYR'S VORTEX.

From David Hodosh Black:

ZEUGLODONS PICK AND JAB QUAVERING ZANTHOXYLUM FLOWERS.

From Rev. Richard F. Olson, S.J.:

JOHN WAS VEXED BY THE FUZZY PTERODACTYL'S MIGHTY QUACK.

From Mrs. Bruce McGill:

QUIZ PALE TOM SAWYER AND VAGUE HUCK FINN ABOUT JOE'S BOX.

From Wilford D. Godbold, Jr.:

UP AT THE ZOO A ROVING OX WAS QUICKLY FED BUG JAM.

From Mrs. H. N. Millard:

JAZZ QUEEN WINS BACK ALIMONY: VEXED FIGHTER PAYS.

From Sidney R. Frank:

ACT FRISKY, JIG ZIPPY, BE AN OX WITH LIQUID VIM.

From Mrs. F. D. Dodge:

A GROUP MAY BE QUICKLY VEXED WITH JAZZ FANS.

From Marie Anderson:

JUST BE VERY QUICK WHEN FIXING ZIP CODE MAIL.
THE CRAZY MEXICANS VOW BY GOD TO QUIP FLIP JOKING.
TEX, A LAZY FAKE IN VULGAR PJ'S MADE BAR-B-Q CHOW.
FIVE OXEN GAZE DOWN QUICKLY ON EPHRAIM ZIMBALIST JR.
JIM EXPECTED TO FLUNK A BIG QUIZ BUT SHOWS A VICTORY.

From Alan J. Leonard:

THE VEXING WIZARDS QUICKLY JUMPED FOR THE BAG.

From Marvin R. Whipple:

A CHIMPANZEE QUICKLY JABBED HIS FINGER INTO A WAX
VAT.

From Paul D. Hance:

QUICK JOKES MIGHT WAX IF LEAVENED BY PRIZES.
WE FIX PRIZES QUICKLY SODA JOKE MIGHT EVEN BE
CRACKERS.
IF PRIZES VEX, GRIM JOKES DEBAUCH MY TRANQUIL JAWS.

From Daniel Kronish:

FEW CAB DRIVERS ENJOY HEXING PIQUANT, MILKY ZEBRAS.

From Ruth Carson:

A QUIET MAD LYNX JUST CREPT BY THE WALK IN A VERY
HAZY FOG.

From Helene Rivers:

LOVELY WOMEN FIX CHIPPED BLACK QUARTZ.

From Mr. and Mrs. Frank Bingman:

BLOKES WHO MIX JUICY EGGPLANT AND FROZEN SQUASH
VARY.
WHO QUICKLY BOUGHT SIX PIZZAS FROM THE NERVOUS
JUDGE.

ASK A DEJECTED PREXY, "WHO ENLIVENED THE GAME OF BEZIQUE?"

WRY QUIPS OF JAZZ COMBOS VEX OLD KNIGHTS.

CZECH SQUAWK BOXES DROOL EMPTY FOREIGN JIVE.

From Mr. and Mrs. Peter W. Smith:

A QUEER MAUVE OWL KEPT BOXES OF ZINC, HAY, AND GRAPE JUICE.

From Nancy A. Church:

WE JUXTAPOSE HIGH-CLASS QUIZ KIDS FROM NEARBY VALLEYS.

From Leah Gailey:

A LEWD, PEEVISH QUEEN AM GOT CRAZY FOR JUKE BOX.

A BIG, DOPEY CHEF KEPT VIGIL ON QUEER, WAX JAM ZONES.

From E. E. Rehmus:

WRY JINX: VAGS BLOCK HUMP'D FEZ (Q.T.)

From S. R. Dunlap:

JUVENILE INK FIGHTS GO BIG WITH CRAZY MIXED UP SQUIDS.

ROVER JUST DOZES AGAIN BUT THE QUICK FOX LIMPS AWAY.

From Gerald Baker:

MY GIRL WOVE SIX DOZEN PLAID JACKETS BEFORE SHE QUIT.

REVIEW THE DAMP JUNGLE ROCKS BEFORE THE NEXT QUIZ.

A DOZEN GAY FOX JOCKEYS LIVED BACK WHERE THE MAPS QUIT.

TAXI DRIVERS WALK QUICKLY BACK UP FROM THE JUNGLE ZOO.

WE AMAZED CLEVER FOLKS BY JUST QUITTING THE SAXO-PHONE.

I'VE BEEN VEXED JUST MAKING FUZZY CIPHERS WITH NO QUILL.

BY JOVE! WHO'D TAX CRAZY QUILTS FROM PEKING?

BUT EVEN HIS EX-WIFE KEPT CAJOLING THE DIZZY GLAMOR QUEEN.

BEES WERE FLYING LAZILY UP OVER A QUEER JACK-IN-THE-BOX.

FOREIGN JOKERS HEXED THE CHAMP BY WAVING A QUALITY FEZ.

From H. Shosteck:

QUEER BRAWNY OXEN PUMP AS THELMA GOES TO ZVICKS-FJORD.

From Karla and Lisa Dieckmann:

A JOYFUL KING WITH A ROYAL ZAX PASSED BY MY QUIET CAVE.

VIVID, LUMPY ZEBRAS OFTEN QUIT JOKING TO CHEW WAX.

A QUAIL, FROG, OX AND LAMB PLAYED WITH JACKS AT A ZOO.

From Florence L. Kite:

FIX UP A DOZEN BIG WATCHES VERY QUICKLY, JIM.

From R. M. Tremayne:

A GYM FIX, WHEN PROVED, JOLTS QUIZ BACKERS.

From Philip S. Mumford:

JOHN VOWED QUINCY KEPT FROZEN BAGEL MIXES.

Several respondents made it clear that they would like to either elaborate on the whole frightening situation, or provide some kind of incisive commentary to go along with it. For instance, Lewis Richmond, writing from the hallowed sanctity of Harvard Yard insisted on providing a sentence with all 43 keys of the typewriter involved. His sentence, he explains, is about a precocious Pilgrim child who, after the manner of his elders, sought to hoodwink the poor Indians further. But his own infantile standards of value brought down the wrath of the Indians upon his scalp. The sentence:

Phlegmy, J. V. Fitz (c. 1625–7) squawk'd, "Bronx: 34½¢?"

Barbara Kraft ran into a situation which indicates the growing conformism of the corporation man. She rode down in an elevator with a young man in a gray flannel suit, carrying the usual attaché case, and studying a legal-size sheet of paper, on which was typed over and over again:

NOW IS THE TIME FOR ALL GOOD MEN TO COME TO THE AID OF THE GROUP.

Maurice Siegel sent along a TWX test sentence which came in over the wires at a time when the circuits kicked up and went out of order:

THE KWIQUE BROUNNE FOKCS JUMPT OURVRE A LAEZIE DOUGUE,S BACH

"By some quirk of electronic impulses," he writes, "it comes out in something that contains English, French, German, and I do believe, a form of the Chaucerian."

Bernard Lee sends along an actual telegram purported to have been intercepted in which the bandit J. Mev instructs his cohort, Zilch, to hide the loot at once:

ZILCH: BURY FT. KNOX SWAG PDQ, J. MEV.

"Please note," Mr. Lee adds, "that this message uses all the letters of the English alphabet once, and only once."

He also claims that while browsing through some old issues of the *New York Times* circa 1916, he saw this obituary and date line:

EX-GOV F. Q. SCHWARTZ, Blindjump, Ky.

W. C. Countess has worked out a phrase which he aptly describes as a Credit Receipt from an emerging nation:

I. O. U. a Zedfkjhgrbqctswvxypmln

He also includes an unlikely Welsh proverb, which he claims means "Loose Burtons are best mended by a Tailor:"

Badfgnxporzvt swckm qije huly

Barbara Mueller, noting that we finally gave up the chase after original, bona fide soda biscuits in favor of gourmet cookies, jibed in a full-alphabet sentence:

WELL BEFORE EXHAUSTIVE MAJOR TRY, THE LAZY, INEXPERIENCED SODA CRACK QUESTOR GAVE UP.

And from Dr. E. I. Dobos, of Denver, who describes himself as a half-baked informer, we received further elucidation about the definition of biscuits. The word "biscuit," he points out, is the Latin version of the German Zwieback, and both mean "baked twice"—Bis-coctus, and Zwei-back. The latter is baked in a loaf, sliced after, and then toasted. The biscuit, because of having the texture of rusk, was so named—disregarding the baking procedure.

We were also tapped lightly on the wrist by the entire resources of the institution known as the Self-Rising Flour and Corn Meal Program, which is sponsored by the American Corn Millers' Federation and the National Soft Wheat Millers' Association.

They wrote me: "Egads, sir! You cannot find a biscuit and this being Biscuit/Muffin Month? The wrath of Zeus shall undoubtedly fall upon mankind for his forgetfulness. Who can forget the biscuits that are a part of the meal—the small, round, flaky biscuits that were smothered with butter and homemade jam or jelly? That, sir, is a biscuit! You can't define a biscuit, although Webster is technically correct, for each region supplies its own label when it comes to biscuits. For example, southern biscuits are relatively flat while northern bakers prefer to make them thicker. But, in every instance a biscuit is a biscuit—it cannot be a cookie or a cracker.

"You are right about there being no soda biscuit, *per se*, on the market today, but boy-oh-boy you sure can find enough flour and mixes to whip up your own batch. Whenever we have a splitting headache, we don't reach for the sodium bicarbonate, we grab a biscuit. Even the centaur would approve of that!"

The only problem I have is that every time I grab a biscuit now, I get a headache.

chapter thirteen

TOM SWIFT AND HIS
ADVERB MACHINE

Note to Game Maniacs:

You have already probably suffered through the
Tom Swifty syndrome, and therefore this chapter will only serve to reinfect you with its viru-
lence. If you care to contract the disease again,
there are some games worked out for you on page
192.

I first ran into the habit-forming game known as *Tom Swifties* while riding in on the train with Gil Fates, the Goodson-Todman producer who has been pushing such shows as *I've Got a Secret, What's My Line?* and others high on the rating meters. Fates mentioned that his whole office had been going out of its mind trying to create choice bits of dialogue for the game, which combines the old Tom Swift form of dialogue with totally ridiculous verbs, adverbs, and phrases. (Example: "I'm a plumber," he piped. Or: "My name is Bridge," he said archly.)

It got its start on the air after panelist Bill Cullen, of *I've Got a Secret,* saw the game mentioned in a newspaper that neither he nor anyone else on his staff could remember. (Some thought it was the Manchester *Guardian,* which Cullen enjoys. More likely, it was the Minneapolis *Tribune,* in which columnist Will Jones had been toying with the game for some time.)

Goodson-Todman adapted the idea for an upcoming show and, in the process, staff members caught the bug. They've been turning out their own candidates for the Tom Swifty list. Among Fates' favorites:

"That makes 144," he said grossly.

"I drove from Maine to California," he stated.

"Let's have some coffee," he spouted.

"That dog has no pedigree," he muttered.

"Enough of your fairy tales," he said grimly.

"Stop hounding me," he barked.

"Turn the thermostat down," he said heatedly.

"You are not permitted to cross the border," he said guardedly.

"We have a goodly supply of ice cubes," he replied coldly.

"You have a sharp sense of humor," he remarked pointedly.

"Pass me the lemons," he said acidly.

"Listen to the birdies sing," she chirped.

"Give it to me on the level," he said flatly.

"Quick, Watson, the needle," he said in a serious vein.

"It's Greenwich time," I mean.

"Help me into my dress," she snapped.

"I never bathe," he said gamely.

"She couldn't get into her mink," he inferred.

Before it became popular, the game had been known for quite some time in Minneapolis, where it seems to have been born. It was in San Francisco, that a paperback titled *Tom Swifties* was privately printed.

The two circumstances are interestingly related, we learned when we talked to a gentleman named Paul Pease, a copy chief for a San Francisco advertising agency, who confessed to perpetrating the entire scourge. Mr. Pease told us that more than ten years ago his father used to deliver these quotations at the kitchen table, and it became a family game. He was living in Minneapolis at the time, and when he migrated to San Francisco a few years ago the idea of making a book out of the game still haunted him.

Fortunately, Bill McDonough, a friend of his in the advertising business, found himself between assignments, and helped him get the book out. It was illustrated by artist John Larrecq.

The first edition of Tom Swifties privately printed, numbered 5,000 copies, and was snapped up in the Bay area. The trio quickly printed another paperback edition of 100,000 copies. It is still going strong.

"We're having a lot of fun with it," Mr. Pease told us on the phone, "and things look pretty rosy for the future. We're already into greeting cards, turtle-neck sweatshirts—something like the kind Tom Swift used to wear, you might remember—and cocktail napkins, which, of course, Tom would never touch. I like to think of this as a sudden success, but then it actually took eleven years to get moving."

After all our investigation of the Tom Swifty syndrome, we heard later from Marvin Bensman, an English teacher from Sheboygan, Wisconsin. In his letter, he traced the whole history of the game for us, and added, "As an English teacher, I use these Tom Swifties to approach an understanding of the adverb, and the complexities of the native language." In this case, at least, it seems that the race is to the Swifties.

After all the furor finally subsided I took the time to find out the status of the *real* Tom Swift, the creation of the late Edward Stratemeyer, who pounded out the original series from 1910 until 1941 at the rate of two chapters each morning and one each afternoon. Under various pseudonyms, Mr. Stratemeyer wrote over 400 titles, among them the Rover Boys series. The original Tom Swift series began fading around the time of World War II, the author feeling that both the war and the fact that he married Tom off to Mary Nestor did the series in. The latter action seemed to turn Tom into a father image instead of a young hero. However, all is not lost. The new series on Tom Swift, Jr. is moving along at a pace that has already eclipsed the 10,000,000 hard-cover sales of the old books.

"Father was something of an opportunist," Harriet S.

Adams told us. She is the daughter of Mr. Stratemeyer and heads the syndicate that still bears his name. "Along about 1907, he felt that youngsters would be fascinated by science fiction with a young hero. He wrote forty titles, the last being *Tom Swift and His Electric Silencer,* and they all sold about the same number of copies. Many of the titles were rather prophetic, among them *The Submarine Boat, The Diamond Makers, The Photo Telephone,* and *The Television Director.* One invention of Tom's I haven't seen come to life is *The Electric Rifle*—but maybe there is such a thing."

In the new series, carried on by Victor Appleton, Jr., Tom's son is a good deal more sophisticated than his dad. He's now going in for sea copters, space solartrons, and electronic retroscopes. "Today all the new books are checked by a scientist, even though the formula is still about the same," Mrs. Adams told us.

At the present moment, Mrs. Adams isn't sure what effect the Tom Swifties are having on the sales of the books. "I know they're not doing us any harm," she said, "and I've even gotten a few from some of our ten- and eleven-year-old readers. I have a strong feeling that father would have loved them."

I had no sooner reported on the *real* Tom Swift as the work of Edward Stratemeyer, when I found this statement contested by Roger Garis, son of Howard R. Garis, who created the famous Uncle Wiggily stories.

According to Roger Garis, Mr. Stratemeyer did create the original idea, but the first thirty-five books in the series were farmed out to Uncle Wiggily's originator on an outright cash basis, with the elder Mr. Garis pounding out four chapters a morning.

What's more, as if nothing can be sacred, we are told that the Bobbsey Twins series was also originated by Mr. Stratemeyer, and also farmed out to the elder Garis and his wife in the early stages of the series.

"In all," the son of Uncle Wiggily's creator tells us, "my father wrote about 500 books, my mother about 200. It was a most interesting period of authorship."

For months, the mail bag was filled with new ideas. Bea Shaw, of North Hollywood, for instance, was not content with singles. She went on to concoct a full conversation piece:

"What are you up to?" she demanded loftily.

"Just staring out the window," he replied painfully.

"So what's the problem?" she asked testily.

"I belong on the top," he said spinning, "I'm brilliant," he glared.

"Then why the beef?" she asked cowed.

"I'm broke," he snapped.

"You have your job at the drugstore," she countered.

"That's incidental," he said through clenched teeth.

"Look how long it took Sinatra," she said frankly.

"I'll have my name in lights," he glowed.

"Just like Cary," she granted.

In her letter, Miss Shaw wrote, "I started to end this with: 'Just like Rock, she granite'—but then we'd have to start a whole new game, wouldn't we? I wish I'd never heard of this!"

That's the trouble with these twisters. Once you're hooked, you're done for.

In fact, Adele Bercovici discovered a real, unintentional "Swifty" in the book *The Latest Continent* by Walker Chapman: "the earth is spherical," D'Ailly stated flatly.

But maybe Dick Marsh of Detroit, has arrived at an ample benediction for the Swifties wave. He suggests that they be confined to single-word quotes only, calling them "Tom Swiftiers."

"Heavens," she said loftily.

"Hell," he said hotly.

"Well," she said deeply.

"How?" he asked bravely.

To which we might add: "Overdone," he said crisply.

If you haven't already done so, you can get a copy of the original Tom Swifties book by sending a dollar to: Tom Swifties, 857 Montgomery Street, San Francisco, 11, California.

For the sake of the well-worn record, we list just a fraction of these adverbial adventures we've received:

From Arthur Rye:

"At last I got my radio to working well," said Tom exstatically.

"You should have given me a DOUBLE raise in spades," said Tom morbidly.

"My German doctor keeps telling me I have an Oedipus complex," muttered Tom.

From Miriam Rappaport:

"Stop staring at me through that keyhole," she said in a fit of pique.

"We breed pigs without vocal chords," he said, disgruntled.

"I've lost my gavel," he expounded.

"I sent my check to the wrong charity," she said with misgiving.

"I found your graduation certificate in the garret," she said diplomatically.

"I was Mussolini's executioner," he deduced.

"I never seem to get a hand with jacks, queens, and kings," he said tenaciously.

"How can I possibly wear such tight pants?" she burst out.

"Let me turn off the dynamo," he said degenerately.

From Frank Duane:

"I wonder what Eve is going to bring for dinner," said Adam fruitlessly.

"Go left if you want to, but the other three went this way," said Tom forthrightly.

From Elizabeth Latimer:

"I once had a lion for a pet," he said offhandedly.

From the Ninth Grade Advanced English Students at Amherst Junior High, Snyder, New York:

"The organ is broken," he piped.

"The evergreen is gone," he pined.

"The pony has gone wild," he said hoarsely.

"Where's my brandy," he sniffed.

"This examination is impossible," she said testily.

"Can't you sew?" she needled.

"What is the largest ocean?" he asked specifically.

"I hit my head on the window," he said painfully.

"The furnace is smoking again," he fumed.

"We'll rip off the shingles," they decided.

"I don't have a thing in my closet," she said unwarily.

"I want a hot dog," he said frankly.

"I'm getting dressed," he panted.

From Dave Fulghum:

"What a melancholy hamlet," he said disdainfully.

"I just burned myself," he said sincerely.

From M. Kaufman:

"This year, June will follow April," he said dismayingly.

"This rocket fell out of the air," he said exorbitantly.

"Look under the green jello," he said sublimely.

"How do you get this horse to stop?" he asked woefully.

"This package is from Europe," he said importantly.

"Why did you remove the ivy?" she asked divinely.

"A bottle is missing from the wine cellar," he said dispiritedly.

"Naomi's daughter-in-law is missing," he said ruthlessly.

From Mrs. Albert Koehl:
"Hot Dog!" he said with relish.
"Mush!" he shouted huskily.

From Alan D. Karasik:
"Drop your gun!" he said disarmingly.
"Never!" he shot back.
"Touché!" he cried penetratingly.
"It's time for your penicillin," injected the nurse.
"How often do you publish?" he asked weakly.

From Evelyn R. Llewellyn:
"I'll take the apartment," he said flatly.
"I've lost my billfold," he said as he pursed his lips.
"Turn on the F.M.," he said with a short wave.

From Marilyn Wendell:
"I'm not particularly fond of snakes," she rattled.
"I prefer not to sit in the center section," she sighed.
"I spent the weekend with my aunt and uncle," she related.
"Well, I'm in favor of a final exam," she protested.
"I've just had a serious operation," he said half-heartedly.
"I always enjoy reading Hemingway," he said in earnest.
"I've just completed my autobiography," said Tom self-righteously.
"We must get this to the printers now," she pressed.
"My glasses should arrive tomorrow," he speculated.
"You're nothing but an old goat," she said kiddingly.
"I'll raise your grade to an A," she remarked.

From Lois L. Davis:

"No one watches harness racing any more," he said sulkily.

"My group had 23% more cavities," she said crestfallen.

From Barney Sharin:

"We've reached the end of the canal," he Said.

"You're running up big bills again," he charged.

"That's a good yolk," he cracked.

From Sonja Coryat:

"I've got eighteen kids," she sighed overbearingly.

"You need an operation," the doctor announced inhospitably.

"Let's go to a Chinese restaurant," he said wantonly.

"I hate autumn," he said rakishly.

"I can't eat starchy foods," he said stiffly.

"Liver is good for your blood," he said ironically.

"I tripped," he said lamely.

From Frederick G. Marks, Jr.:

"I have a bad heart," he murmured.

"Your premium is overdue," they said collectively.

"You seem to have outgrown your pants," he said measuredly.

"Don't needle me," he said pointedly.

From Gerald Baker:

"Speak softly and carry a big stick," he said bashfully.

"I swallowed a lot of hay," he said balefully.

"I wish I had a boutonnière," he said lackadaisically.

From William E. Davis:

"I ate too much corn," he said huskily.

"This sausage really has a lot of flavor," he said sagely.

"Your dress is a little tight," he observed fittingly.

"You might try looking in the attic," he said loftily.

From Robin F. Brancato:

"You never catch any fish," she carped.

"One of my ribs is missing!" he cried adamantly.

"You've used my bubble bath," she foamed.

"Your horse always comes in last," she nagged.

"You've got too much rouge on, ma'am," he said cheekily.

From Delight Ansley and Marie Longyear:

"My name is Yul Brynner," he stated baldly.

"We've struck oil!" he gushed.

"I'm dying," he croaked.

From Naomi Schlain:

"My suit's too tight," he burst forth.

From Juliana Buonocore:

"I didn't have time to mow the lawn," he hedged.

From Frances Bonney:

"Have you the tweezer?" she implied.

"I'll slip into my bikini," she said briefly.

From Frances Davidson:

"That's a very Freudian remark," she said dreamily.

"Don't forget to add some Worcestershire," she said saucily.

"You must take this examination," the teacher said testily.

From Robert M. Worcester:

"Get those birds on the fly," he groused.

"Take my picture," she snapped.

From Nin Burnett:

"I had it sauté meunière," he said soulfully.

"I fixed the plumbing," he said flushing.

From M. G. Houston:

"These are my grandparents," he said with forbearance.

"I'm a buck private," he said without rancor.

"I will never be a street-walker again," she said inexorably.

"I must reduce," he said fatuously.

From Molly Coates:

"Do you have to have an operation?" she inquired cuttingly.

"No, I twisted my ankle," he replied limply.

"You mean you have a fracture?" she asked brokenly.

From William H. Cullen:

"This is the dive I got drunk in," he said disjointedly.

From Lyle L. Erb:

"I think Shakespeare is obscene," he said, learingly.

"Anatole France was an angel," she asserted, revoltingly.

And to top off a combination, Frances Benninger uses Tom Swifties to provide captions for book jackets in the high school library at Brookville, Pennsylvania:

TREASURE ISLAND—"Accidents will happen," Captain Hook said offhandedly.

LEGEND OF SLEEPY HOLLOW—"I just lost my head," Ichabod said absent-mindedly.

ADVENTURES OF SHERLOCK HOLMES—"Quick, Dr. Watson, the needle," he said in a serious vein.

OLE YELLER—"This dog has no pedigree," he muttered.

COOKBOOK—"There's something wrong with this pineapple," she said dolefully.

TRAPPING—"Did you get the mink?" he asked furtively.

TOOLS—"Did you get the point?" he asked sharply.

BIOGRAPHY OF ALEXANDER GRAHAM BELL—"Give me a ring," she said phonily.

DRIVER TRAINING—"You're a good driver," she said automatically, *or* "I just made a U (ewe) turn," he said sheepishly.

MISCELLANEOUS—"This is a good book," he said readily.

FAIRY TALES—"Enough of your fairy tales," he said grimly.

GEOMETRY—"I'm going around in circles in geometry," she said figuratively.

FOOTBALL—"I get a kick out of football," he said gamely.

GHOST STORY—"How about a ghost story?" Miss Long asked spritely.

MATH—"That makes 144," he said grossly.

GAMES FOR CHAPTER THIRTEEN

Tom Swifties are twisted adverbs or phrases, describing the way a person says something. Examples: "Pass me the lemons," he said acidly. Or: "Stop hounding me," he barked. Or: "I never bathe," he said gamely.

Here's a list of adverbs for you to go ahead and make up your own do-it-yourself kit of Swifties. Good luck.

—— he said grossly
—— he stated
—— he spouted
—— he muttered
—— he said heatedly
—— he charged
—— he said in a serious vein
—— he snapped
—— he inferred
—— he said loftily
—— he said hotly
—— he said deeply
—— he said crisply
—— he said morbidly
—— he said fruitlessly
—— he said hoarsely
—— he said frankly
—— he said unwarily
—— he said woefully
—— he said sulkily
—— he said pointedly

Excellent 20
Good 15
Fair 10

Now try it the other way. Here's a list of sentences for which you can apply your own Swifty:

"I tripped," he said ——
"Don't needle me," he said ——
"Your premium is overdue," they said ——
"I swallowed a lot of hay," he said ——
"I like to play the organ," he ——
"You might try looking in the attic," he said ——
"You never catch any fish," she ——
"You've struck oil," she ——
"You must take this exam," the teacher said ——
"Don't forget to add Worcestershire," she said ——
"You've got too much rouge on," he said ——
"You've used my bubble bath," she ——
"Take my picture," she ——
"I must reduce," he said ——
"I lost my head," he said ——

Excellent 10
Good 8
Fair 5

chapter fourteen

WITH A SONG, OR A POEM, OR ANYTHING REMOTELY RESEMBLING THESE IN YOUR HEART, OR MIND, OR WHATEVER

Note to Game Maniacs:

You may, if you wish, skip along to page 207 of this chapter, and see where it gets you. We can guarantee that you won't soar on lyrical clouds, but you might find enough discordant cacophony to keep you awake a few moments before dozing off fitfully. The answers, as usual, are buried in the forefront of the chapter, in case you can't figure out the answers by dead reckoning.

Poems and songs are the damndest things, and they're dangerous. What else but these will buzz around in your head for hours, with rhyme usually, yes, but without reason? For instance Harry Coleman once sent me a rhymed invitation to an alumni fund-raising benefit that has bothered me for months. I hope it might do the same to you:

> Get your head off your antimacassar
> And send a nice fat check to Vassar.

After Mary McCarthy's book, Vassar might well use some funds, but not this way. Not with a poem which is as habit-drugging as the famous "Punch conductor, punch with care . . ."

There are other poems that do this to me. Like the one Irby B. Brown sent to me as a "summer replacement for the Purple Cow. . . ."

> My favorite animal, by far,
> Is the South American strickle:
> It looks exactly like Jack Paar
> And tastes like butter brickle.

I wish I could say you can take this or leave it, but if you read it a couple of times, you can't. You'll be haunted in your sleeping and waking hours, and you'll finally have to memorize *Casey at the Bat* in order to get it out of your mind.

George Scarbrough, in Oak Ridge, Tennessee, won't let well enough alone, either. Instead of letting *The Purple Cow* rattle around senselessly in his head, he creates a parody which simply takes over and does exactly the same thing:

> I never saw a purple cow
> Wear a dhoti in a dhow
> If in a dhow, and in a dhoti
> *You* see one, go tug his goatee.

Rhythmic teasers are, in fact, a plague upon this best of all possible worlds. B. S. Stephenson was shown one fifteen years ago by an associate of his at Washington and Lee University, and he hasn't forgotten it since:

> "Simile, der day go
>   Toussain busis inaro."
> "Nojo, demain busis, demis trux
>   Summit cousin, summit dux."

The translation, Mr. Stephenson reports, is:

> "See, Millie, there they go,
>   Thousand buses in a row."
> "No, Joe, them ain't buses, them is trucks,
>   Some with cows, and some with ducks."

Rosemary Corry, whom we have met in a previous chapter with her antics of *Le Petit Théâtre de Vieux Carré* in New Orleans extends her chicanery to a song album which she calls *An Addressograph Operator Sings the Files*. In this unmerciful maneuver, she takes the lyrics from *Pennies from Heaven* and turns them into a highly-unlikely mailing list:

> Avery Thyme
> Etienne Zatarain

> Panis Fromm Evans
> Don Juneau
> "Itch" Cloud
> Con Thames
> Panis Fromm Evans
> Jewel Fein
> Ura Fortune Follen
> Oliver Towne
> Bea Surrat
> Orrie M. Bella
> S. Upside Downs . . .

She not only continues this ballad in such a vein, but proceeds to attack other standards long on the ASCAP list with things like this version of *September Song*:

> Florence A. Long
> Long Thyme Fromm
> May "Tudie" Sempre
> Andy Days . . .

"The Longs and the Fromm families pop up with alarming regularity," says Rosemary Corry.

Master of the readable maze of sounds and rhythm is Ogden Nash, who manages to squeeze an almost uncountable number of metric feet into a single line of poetry. If you ask him how he happened to stumble on this format, he will be frank enough to tell you that the style provided a marvelous cover-up for what he calls his half-baked literacy.

At lunch at the Algonquin, over a baby lamb stew and a noggin of ale, he told me one time: "I just stumbled on the idea when fooling around with light verse, and I suddenly discovered that it gave me a chance to express my own ideas— which were not up to Plato or Santayana—in an inoffensive and unpretentious way. I've been in love with words all my life, and this particular style suddenly seemed to create an outlet for my own limited mentality."

Wearing a hound's tooth tweed jacket, Mr. Nash took a few more bites of his stew and went on. "When you get right down to it," he said, "I suppose all this is really a cover-up for my naked self. It's my own private Society for the Prevention of Embarrassment. And I think it enables me to communicate with the ordinary human being without sounding like an Eddie Guest. In other words, I've got myself off the hook, and I'm able to have the best of two worlds."

There are a great many Ogden Nash fans who will disagree with this modesty of his. The beauty of Nash's style lies in its capacity to fracture the sound barrier, but still maintain full respect for Newtonian physics. His apparent disengagement from poetic discipline is illusory; every line is hammered out in classical tradition. His scansion is perfect.

Mr. Nash prefers to think of his works as "comments in verse" rather than poetry. He feels that pure poetry should be reserved for expressing thoughts raised to heights that haven't otherwise been reached. On the other hand, he insists that his commentary makes a statement of some kind, however minor.

One test of a classic in any category is whether it stands up under scrutiny in different times and places. With the help of Charles Berlitz and the Berlitz School of Languages, I was able to put one of Ogden Nash's poems through the mill of three generations of translation just to see what might happen. Mr. Berlitz, an old Nash admirer himself, saw to it that the poem went first to a French translator, who put it into French. After that, it was translated back to English by another French translator, who passed the new English version to a German translator. Here the process was repeated, with one German translator putting the poem into German, and a different one putting it back into English again. The same steps were taken in Spanish, with step number six being the final translation from Spanish to English.

The poem was a simple and familiar one to old Nashian followers:

> I have a funny daddy
> Who goes in and out with me,
> And everything that baby does
> My daddy's sure to see.
> And everything that baby says
> My daddy's sure to tell.
> You *must* have read my daddy's verse.
> I hope he fries in Hell.

The first English version to come out of the French translation stood up well:

> I have an odd character for a papa,
> Who enters and goes out with me;
> And everything that baby does
> My father sees it surely;
> And everything that baby says
> My father says it surely.
> You must have read the poem of my father:
> I hope he grills in Hell.

The translation from the German stood up well, too. The main change occurs in the last line: "I hope he is deep-frying in Hell," which comes from the line in the German translation: "Ich hoffe, er schmort in der Hölle."

The final translation, from Spanish, remains almost as recognizable as the original—although no attempt was made to go beyond a literal translation at any step:

> I have a father very full of occurrences,
> Who accompanies me wherever I go,
> And everything the little child does
> My father does not fail to see.
> Everything the little child says,
> My father will say the same thing himself.
> You will have to be reading my father's poem.
> I hope they cook him well in Hell.

The Berlitz translators and Mr. Nash have reason to be happy about the whole thing. The former have shown themselves to have keen eyes and ears for idiom; the latter has received fresh evidence that his appeal is universal, in spite of his own misgivings.

When it comes to limericks, we are opening up an entirely new barrel of pickles. That they are habit-forming, no one in his right mind will disagree.

Take Taylor Caldwell, for instance. She confesses that she likes writing limericks as well as she likes writing her novels. She gave me some of her more printable limericks, confessing also that she's written a good many more pungent ones:

> There was a shirt salesman named Speller
> Who suddenly wrote a best seller
> And thought he'd relax,
> But then came Fed tax!
> He's back selling shirts in the cellar.

Others from Miss Caldwell's able pen appear here for the first time anywhere, and are among an original collection which she claims are enough to fill an entire volume:

> There was a young lady whose knees
> Could never endure a brisk breeze;
> She wore woolen pants
> Which did not enhance
> Her chances to *really* unfreeze.

> There was a young damsel named Brooks
> Who was lavishly dowered with looks.
> But when parked in a car
> With her swain she would spar,
> And insist on discussing good books.

"She spent the rest of her life," Miss Caldwell adds, "studying the *Encyclopedia Britannica*—alone."

She also notes that the following originals are not too good, but "rougher:"

> There once was a sheik named Emaybes
> Who bragged he was strong with the ladies,
> His wives in a row
> Then shouted, "That's so?
> Then where in the hell are our babies?"

> There once was a young man too serious,
> Who was guiltless of glances more leerious;
> The girls like him well,
> To each other they'd tell
> "I'm intact—though I find him damned wearious."

In the sliding spectrum of limericks, Miss Caldwell's concern about roughness is unwarranted. For some reason, the limerick form brings out the most impish side of all of us, and often to most forgivable hilarity. Rabbi Charles Mantinband of Hattiesburg, Mississippi, once was inspired to send me this commentary on the limerick:

> A limerick packs laughs anatomical
> Into space that is quite economical
> But the good ones I've seen
> So seldom are clean
> And the clean ones so seldom comical.

Gerard Neyroud likes his limericks in the animal kingdom. (In sending it along, he also invented another brand of chewing gum to supplement Vehemint, for angry people. His is for people who don't like to chew gum, or who want to give up the habit: Eschewing Gum). His limerick:

> Said a saucy young skunk to a gnu
> "You are quite odoriferous; phew!"
> Said the gnu to the skunk:
> "If I stank like you stunk
> "I'd hate to be me were I you!"

In San Francisco, John Coulthard walks the floor at night with a game he calls Limericryptograms. Examples:

> Aim aid din Abe you teepee raid
> Haddock cost tomb in witchy Dis played
> Al ursine aweigh
> Two inn. "Hippo ray!"
> Diddle Ottoman scree, "Mitts sew kay!"

Translation:

> A maid in a beauty parade
> Had a costume in which she displayed
> Allures in a way
> To win, "Hip Hooray!"
> Did a lot o' men scream, "It's okay!"

Or:

> Ey yam knot picanny hoodoo
> But Ike Ann dew moron Ute to.
> Why lit taint two mice tile
> Ide dew wit Dan dyes mile,
> Sew ewe felloes cant oil Abe it, two!

Translation:

> I am not picking any who do,
> But I can do more'n you two.
> While it ain't to my style,
> I do it and I smile,
> So you fellows can toil a bit, too!

Robert Challman, a Ph.D. from Minneapolis, finds restful therapy in creating what he calls Household Poets. For the kitchen, there is Burns; the dining room, Lamb; the bedroom, Lovelace; the nursery, Suckling; the smoking room, Seegar; the laundry, Dryden; and out in the barn, De la Mare.

He is also developing a series of Occupational Poets:

Wordsworth for authors; Donne for bill collectors; Pope for the Catholic clergy; and Longfellow for basketball players.

It wasn't long before this contribution in TRADE WINDS brought a few readers to their feet. Ruth Lesly immediately wanted to know why he forgot Whittier for TV gagwriters. Others responded like this:

From Ely Pilchik:
    For pigeon fanciers   (Homer)
    For peanut vendors   (Shelley)
    For shoeshine boys   (Browning)
    For whalers   (Shakespeare)
    For dog catchers   (Pound)
    For exurban developers   (Holmes)
    For Scotch terrier breeders   (Mac Leish)
    For refrigerator salesmen   (Frost)
    For druggists   (Milton)

From Mrs. Charles Siegel, who would make it Occupational writers:
    For baseball infielders   (Fielding)
    For baseball pitchers   (Thoreau)
    For lecturers   (Remarque)
    For seamstresses   (Hemingway)
    For floor walkers   (Bunyan)
    For soldiers   (Defoe)
    For postmen   (Mailer)
    For family men   (Cozzens)

From Beverly Padwo:
    In the playroom   (Noyes)
    In the library   (Still)
    In the bedroom   (Wilde)

Alvin Tresselt and Duncan Morrison call themselves the two elves who put together *Humpty Dumpty* magazine. They have been grieving for a long time for the poor song writer

who gave up on every song too soon. He's the fellow who refused to go on after he had written such songs as "It's Two
O'Clock in the Morning" and "Tea for Three." The two gentlemen above claim that they have unearthed a trunkful of
old song manuscripts that this mythical tin-eared composer
had written. Among the tattered manuscripts were:

MOON OVER FORT LAUDERDALE
ON THE SIDEWALKS OF NEWARK
SHUFFLE OFF TO SCHENECTADY
BUTTON UP YOUR TOPCOAT
YOU'RE THE CREAM IN MY OATMEAL
THERE'S NO BUSINESS LIKE ACTING BUSINESS
MEET ME IN LOUISVILLE, LOUIE
OH, TO BE IN MINNESOTA IN THE MORNING
A NIGHTINGALE SANG IN HERALD SQUARE
GIVE MY REGARDS TO 42ND STREET
HELLO, DOROTHY
WALKING IN A WONDER WINTERLAND
TWO CIGARILLOS IN THE DARK
COME TO ME MY BLUE BABY

Adele Pavis has developed her own tranquilizer for weary
students with a game she calls Course Songs. For a course in
Measurement and Statistics of Education, she recommends
"What's the Use of Wonderin'?" For a Thesis Seminar, she
suggests "With a Little Bit of Luck"; for Physics, "Till the
End of Time."

Mrs. Charlotte Hermance used to while away her time during college choir rehearsals by developing specialized occupational hymns. Her collection is growing fast:

For dentists — Crown Him with Many Crowns
For bankers — Ten Thousand Times Ten Thousand
For brokers — I Put My Trust in Thee
For bookkeepers — A Charge to Keep, Have I
For bakers — I Need Thee Every Hour

For astronauts — Rise Up, O Men of God
For archeologists — Rock of Ages

And thus we close our song and poem section, but not without an additional word. Samuel Livingston advises me that there's a legend that whenever Bach worked on his composing away from home at his studio, he would develop a tremendous appetite. He finally tired of going home every day for lunch, and packed it every day to take with him. From that time on, gentle reader, it became known as a Bach's lunch.

GAMES FOR CHAPTER FOURTEEN

Take the famous old poem "I Never Saw a Purple Cow." It goes like this:

> I never saw a purple cow
> I never hope to see one
> But I can tell you anyhow
> I'd rather see than be one.

Pass this around to your guests, or if you're alone, pass it around to yourself, and see if you can make up an equally ridiculous poem, using only the first line of this one.

Translate the following poem into English, recognizing that it is written in garbled, ungrammatical phonetics.

> "Simile, der day go
>   Toussain busis inaro."
> "Nojo, demain busis, demis trux
>   Summit cousin, summit dux."

Excellent	1 minute
Good	2 minutes
Fair	3 minutes

The following looks like a list of names. But it isn't. It is a garbled phonetic version of the lyrics of a popular standard song. See if you can translate the lyrics, and identify the song.

Avery Thyme

Etienne Zatarain
Panis Fromm Evans

Do the same thing for another popular standard:

Florence A. Long
Long Thyme Fromm
May "Tudie" Sempre

Excellent	10 seconds
Good	8 seconds
Fair	6 seconds

Make up last lines for these three limericks of Taylor Caldwell's:

> There was a shirt salesman named Speller
> Who suddenly wrote a best seller
> And thought he'd relax,
> But then came Fed tax!
> ------------------------------
> There was a young lady whose knees
> Could never endure a brisk breeze;
> She wore woolen pants
> Which did not enhance
> ------------------------------
> There was a young damsel named Brooks
> Who was lavishly dowered with looks.
> But when parked in a car
> With her swain she would spar
> ------------------------------

Translate this garbled phonetic limerick into some kind of meaning:

> Aim aid din Abe you teepee raid
> Haddock cost tomb in witchy Dis played
> Al ursine aweigh

Two inn, "Hippo ray!"
Diddle Ottoman scree, "Mitts sew kay!"

Or this:

> Ey yam knot picanny hoodoo
> But Ike Ann dew moron Ute to.
> Why lit taint two mice tile
> Ide dew with Dan dyes mile
> Sew ewe felloes cant oil Abe it, two!

Excellent	1 minute
Good	2 minutes
Fair	3 minutes

If Burns is the poet laureate of the kitchen; Lamb, for the dining room; Lovelace the bedroom; Suckling, the nursery—find a poet to go along with the following:

For pigeon fanciers ——
For peanut vendors ——
For shoeshine boys ——
For whalers ——
For dog catchers ——
For exurban developers ——
For refrigerator salesmen ——

Excellent	6
Good	5
Fair	4

Now do the same things for any kind of author, poet or not. (Examples: For baseball infielders, Fielding; for the playroom, Noyes.)

For baseball pitchers ——
For lecturers ——
For seamstresses ——
For floorwalkers ——

For soldiers ——
For postmen ——
For family men ——

Excellent	5
Good	3
Fair	2

Once upon a time there was a faint-hearted song writer who kept giving up on the verge of success. Two of his notable failures were: "It's Two O'Clock in the Morning," and "Tea for Three."

Can you make up your own list of other failures they might have written? For a start, you can consider "The Sidewalks of Newark."

Excellent	10
Good	8
Fair	5

Hymns can be utilized for occupational purposes, in gentle fun which would not offend the parsonage. Can you find an occupation to go with the following hymns? (Example: Crown Him With Many Crowns—for dentists)

Ten Thousand Times Ten Thousand, for ——
I Put My Trust in Thee, for ——
A Charge to Keep, Have I, for ——
I Need Thee Every Hour, for ——
Rise Up, Oh Men of God, for ——
Rock of Ages, for ——

Excellent	5
Good	4
Fair	3

chapter fifteen

POTABLE POTPOURRI, OR
HOW I LIED TO
MY DEAR DEAD ACCOUNTANT

Note to Game Maniacs:

Your appointed task is almost completed, if indeed you have got this far. For your final fling, the game section is more or less sprinkled through the entire chapter. We trust you've enjoyed this gambol through the maze of verbiage, in spite of whatever sleep you might have lost in the process.

Inside trade jokes of any classification are usually more fun than a monkey filled with a barrel of beer. Usually, they need only a little explanation, and then the uninitiated can understand them as well as the expert in the field.

Show business, of course, is bound to be one place where the inside joke flourishes, what with the legions of creative talent that flock to its temples.

One showbiz story revolves around the ubiquitous trunk in which vaudeville players are always supposed to carry their props and other belongings.

A performer was explaining to the stage manager that he had to have his trunk just offstage, in the wings, regardless of the fact that the wings were already jammed with scenery.

"What's your act?" asked the harassed stage manager.

"It's a trick act," said the trouper. "I hit myself on the head ten times with a sledge hammer."

"You've got the sledge hammer right in your hand," snapped the stage manager. "What have you got in the trunk that's so important?"

"Headache powder," said the performer, and went out to do his act.

Agents of every description are always coming in for their share of showbiz jokes, probably because of the many frustrations of their ulcer-producing trade.

One actor's agent was on the verge of suicide because he was unable to sign up enough worthwhile talent. Even his avocation—that of a Democratic ward heeler—was not enough to take the sting out of the prospect of giving up his whole career. When he was just at the point of throwing in the sponge, the phone rang. It was a famous star, who happened to be a Republican.

"Heard a lot about you," said the star, "and I was thinking maybe I might let you be my agent. Interested?"

"Am I *interested?*" said the agent. "I'll be over in three minutes."

"Just one thing," said the star. "You're not a Democrat, are you?"

After a short pause, the agent's voice came back on the phone. "Not necessarily," he said.

A sub-species of the show business joke is the Hollywood joke. One of these concerns Darryl Zanuck, who was screening hundreds of rare and unusual acts for a giant film extravaganza. One of them happened to be an elephant, which could do a perfect imitation of Bing Crosby singing, Paul Newman acting, and Gene Kelly dancing. After watching the elephant do all this perfectly, Zanuck said:

"Sorry, we're all jammed up with too many imitators. You'll have to come back when you learn to be yourself."

One of the pillars of show business is a gentleman whom the public rarely hears about, but who heads up one of the largest talent agencies in the country. He is Abe Lastfogel, head of William Morris, Ltd., and his capacity for being seen anyplace at any time has built up many legends about him. Though old hat to the trade, they are not widely known among non-pros.

One story has it that two actors were visiting Rome, when they encountered a huge crowd in the square. They climbed to a balcony to get a better view, not knowing that the celebration was for the Pope.

One of the actors nudged the other and said, "Who is that gentleman in purple standing beside Abe Lastfogel?"

According to the other story, a tourist, driving in the vicinity of Springfield, Illinois, came upon a man splitting rails. He stopped his car and said: "I beg your pardon, sir, but you look familiar. What is your name?"

"Abe," said the rail-splitter, continuing to whack away at the wood.

The tourist's jaw fell open. "You're not Abe *Lincoln*, are you?"

"No," said the rail-splitter. "Abe Lastfogel. William Morris, Limited."

Another giant institution of show business is MCA, often known as the Star-Spangled Octopus. When it bought its building at 57th and Madison Avenue, it was buzzed about that the reason for buying it was that there was a Chase Manhattan Bank on the first floor, and MCA would be able to build a chute into which to drop its money. The offices are plush, deep-carpeted, and furnished with rare antiques. The rumor is that some people have sunk so deeply in the carpets, they haven't been heard from since. The building happens to be directly opposite the IBM Building, where the THINK signs originated.

Latest report is that MCA has countered this with signs on every desk reading: DON'T THINK—*SELL*.

Whenever a film is made, the executives involved make it a

ritual to screen the "rushes"—that film footage which represents the day's shooting. During the filming of a big Biblical spectacular, one director enthusiastically watched a scene about Moses, then left the screening room quickly to wire the New York office: MOSES LOOKS GREAT IN THE RUSHES.

Ezra Goodman's book *The Fifty-Year Decline and Fall of Hollywood* has a couple of inside definitions in its pages. An assistant producer is a mouse, studying to be a rat, while an associate producer is "the only one who will associate with the producer."

In the theater, the most nerve-wracking of all times is the pre-Broadway tryout in New Haven.

During one such tryout, a frenzied call to New York was made to get a replacement for an ailing actor who had only one line to say: "Hark, I hear the cannon's roar."

The replacement actor rehearsed this single line for half a day, without the sound effect, and was then shoved onstage in front of the audience to hear the stage cannon go off in his ear.

"What the *hell* is *that?*" he yelled.

Show business, of course, has no corner on the market for inside jokes, although some yarns in other categories spill over into the show business scene. For instance, there's the one about the downcast actor who went to a psychiatrist.

"I'm in a mess," said the actor. "I'm cast in a musical, but I can't carry a tune, I can't dance, I can't remember my lines, I'm too nervous to do anything right—and I really can't even act."

"I would suggest," said the psychiatrist, "that you give up show business."

"I can't," said the actor. "I'm a star."

Printers, of course, are not without their share of inside jokes. One of the better known type faces is called Goudy, and during the setting up in type of a series of books on philosophy, one Linotype operator put up a sign over his machine reading: NIETZSCHE BUT NOT GOUDY.

By the same token, film editors often break up their routine with ridiculous signs. One film editor at NBC-TV news was snowed with the work of putting the sound track in exact accord with the picture, a process known as "synching." He comforted himself with a sign reading: I SYNCH, THEREFORE I AM.

Madison Avenue has its own trade jokes, but in addition, it has its language. I was exposed to it at one time, and finally decided to incorporate the entire language into one memo. It wasn't very difficult to do:

MEMO TO: Almost Anybody
SUBJECT: Anything Appropriate
CLASSIFICATION: GENERAL ALL-PURPOSE MEMO

You will recall that we've been firming up this problem for some time, and just in the nature of pitching up a few mashie shots to see if we come near the green, I'd like to express these angles:

First, I think we should take a reading of the whole general situation to see if it is being spitballed correctly so that we can eventually wham it through for approval or disapproval as the case might be. In other words, we've got to live with this for a long time, and there are certain rock-bottom slants which we will have to try on for size. Since this situation hits us where we live, and since it has to be geared-in before we hit the stretch, it is only logical that we throw in a few cross-bucks before we take it off-tackle. I can't help feeling that we're all soft as a grape at this stage of the game, and unless we want to get caught with our metaphors down, we'd better get the egg off our faces and the cablestitch sweaters off our teeth.

If we're going to romance this thing, we've got to avoid the double whammy, or it's liable to turn into the kiss of death. Now that we're getting to the short strokes, we'd better see that the lock-up sings with a sizzle at the same time we move in on it.

The best way to flirt with it, as I see it, is to give it the work-over just about the time we're ready to segue into it. I think we all realize that this might be throwing some curves, but in a situation like this, it's a question of hit or get off the plate. This is a shirt-sleeve problem, and we've got to put on our gum boots and wade into it. Let's face it—when we're nosing down into the grass roots like this we're going to be lucky to pushbutton it before we ride herd at an all-around group noodling session.

In other words, we might get caught off first base, and the whole thing might go over like a lead balloon. So let me urge that we all kick this around and put on our creative thinking caps so that all of us will profit in the final wrap-up.

Just so we set this thing straight, I think it advisable that we all crowd in for a firm-up, at which time there will be a full spell-out.

On an evening when conversation seems sparse, you might try asking each of your guests to recall any special trade jokes of their own calling, which will either succeed in brightening up an otherwise dull evening—or breaking the party up fast.

The same might apply to any of the following games, which are tortuous enough in their own right. For instance, Dave Garroway and TV producer Ted Mills started a game once which sounds innocent enough, but unless you're on your toes, it can get you into trouble. It's called FOR A DOLLAR . . . and you must play it with one other person over a long period of time in order either to come out even, or at least without losing your shirt. The rules are simple: At any time at all, you can say to your partner: "For a dollar—answer this question."

Then you throw at him a legitimate question for which you have the clear and legitimate answer firmly tucked in your cranium. If he can't answer it, he gives you a dollar. If he does answer it, you give him a dollar. But you are now also vulnerable, for he is privileged to ask you a question in return, and if you fail to answer, you owe him a dollar. What happens is that hundreds of thousands of dollars can change hands in this kind of acrobatics, and if you've chosen your partner well, you usually come out about even. Disputes constantly arise about the validity of the question asked, and this is one of the more delicate points of the game. For instance, if your partner asks: "Who won the curling championship of Hungary in 1931?" the chances are that you'd have a legitimate beef. On the other hand, if you're equipped with some equally esoteric information, you can quickly neutralize his question, and you end up owing each other a dollar. The main warning about this game is to make sure you've got a lot of tough questions with the accurate answer in mind, so that you can throw them back after you've been put on the defensive. And remember—neither party can ask two questions in a row, so there is a cushion of protection for you if things get too rough.

Another game making the rounds is called DICTIONARY —usable for a friendly gathering which may just change character after the game gets going. The hostess (or why not the host—he never seems to get involved in this sort of thing, and it's about time that he did) passes out a sheet of paper and pencil to each guest. (Did you ever, though, find enough pencils and paper to go around when you wanted them? It's a ridiculous assumption to think that you'll have this hardware handy, but let's assume it anyway.) Now—the person who is elected THAT (as opposed to IT. It's about time people stopped being chosen IT. There is something so degrading about IT.) takes a giant, economy-sized dictionary and looks up the toughest word he or she can find. And *really* tough. A word that even a Phi Bete is not likely to know.

Let's say the word—if this isn't too easy—is *strobila,* which means a linear series of similar structures, or a chain of larval scyphozoan jellyfishes. (If any of your group know this word, they ought to be drummed out of the club.)

The next step for the THAT to do is to instruct every one of the guests (if any are left) to write down the word—and beside it write a definition of the word which *sounds,* at least, like a real dictionary definition. Since most of the guests will not know the word, the idea is to *bluff* the definition in the most legitimate-sounding way possible, with the object being to fool the rest of the guests into thinking your definition is right.

At this point, the THAT collects all the bluff and/or real definitions, and filters into them the actual dictionary definition. The THAT then reads off the definitions, and the rest of the guests try to guess which one is real and which isn't. It is surprising how many of the bluff definitions sound so genuine that it is impossible to tell which is real and which isn't. For instance, at one gathering, the following bluff definitions were handed in:

STROBILA

—of or pertaining to *trobia,* an ancient Egyptian ceremony still celebrated among certain desert tribes today.

—a natural phenomenon caused by a chemical reaction resulting from certain sodium compounds, heated to 2000 degrees F., or above.

—a distortion of the spectrum caused by electro-magnetic impulses in a gravitational field.

—a rare tropical fish of South America, now almost extinct.

—the act or fact of vacillation, as applied to muscular spasm.

—part of the laboratory process in the development of

DNA, prior to the separation of the genetic structure.

You will note that nearly all of these have an authoritative ring which would have a good chance of fooling anyone but an expert in the areas involved.

Anyway, that's the game, and if you get tangled up in it you do so at your own risk.

Charlotte Bingham, the young English author, has a game which might well blossom into another Tom Swifty syndrome, if not quickly eradicated. It's relatively simple, and as they say in the party books, it provides hilarious fun and joviality.

You understand, I'm not guaranteeing that, I'm simply quoting a phrase that you're bound to run into in this sort of book, and I felt the pages should not be closed without resorting to it. For the want of a better title, we might call this ACT IT OUT. This is the way Miss Bingham explains it:

"Take a ridiculous description from a book—then try to act it out. Here's one: 'He had a slightly sardonic look playing around his lips.' Now—" continues Miss Bingham, "I defy you to show that expression. Or this one: 'She nodded delicately, with a wispy veil over her eyes.'"

This may take a little research, but the conscientious hostess—if there are any left—might comb through a few novels, pull out phrases like this, pass them around the coffee table, and see what comes out. With the general level of literature today, no hostess should have to go past page three before she finds an adequate amount of literary phrases.

In a novel published by Farrar, Straus, and Giroux, there's a devastating game available, if you're of a mind to stick your neck out. It is called THE GAME OF DOSTOEVSKY, from the novel of the same name by Samuel Astrachan. The game is played with dice on a board you can shape up on a piece of shirt cardboard in the twinkling of your superego. You make seven squares along each of the four edges. You fill the lower right hand corner in with GO. Each of the other squares you label in consecutive order: SLOTH, ENVY, GLUTTONY, ANGER, LUST, GRACE, COVETOUSNESS, PRIDE, SLOTH, ENVY, GLUTTONY, ETC—repeating the same order until you run out of squares.

One person is appointed the Grand Inquisitor, who judges the player's success or failure. Each player is given two symbols —one to mark his progress on the board, and the other to indicate how many turns he has made around the board.

The first time he comes around back to the GO corner, he puts his symbol under the *D* in Dostoevsky, which is printed in the middle of the board. The first player to move past the *Y* in that name loses.

Starting at GO, each player throws the dice and then moves his symbol clockwise to the indicated square. He must then confess to whatever "sin" his throw lands him on, in the name of a character from a previously determined play or novel. The confession may last for no more than a minute, and is judged by the Grand Inquisitor, who may award the player a Grace Card or penalize him by making him throw the dice again. The Grace Card may be held indefinitely, though no player may have more than one at a time, or may be used whenever the player wishes. For example, if he lands on a "sin" to which he is not prepared to confess, he may turn in his Grace Card to the Grand Inquisitor and return to the nearest Grace Corner. Or if he throws an eleven or twelve he may prefer to turn in his card and go back to a Grace Corner rather than move so far ahead on the board.

Of course, if you *really* want to lose friends and alienate people, forget the fictional character involved, and make everybody make his own confession for the square he lands on. This could lead to the multiple dissolution of the group in nothing flat. Or it's probably safer to go out and buy a second-hand Parchesi board.

A. C. Spectorsky brought to light a magnificent game while preparing material for his classic *The Exurbanites*. It's a simple form of torture, a little less comfortable than subjecting the victim to the stretching racks or sealing him in an Iron Maiden.

The victim is brought into a room and told that the rest of the group has made up a story. He is to ask questions which can be answered "yes" or "no," and thus discern the pattern of the story.

Actually, no story exists. Whenever the victim asks a question ending with a consonant, the group answers "yes." Whenever the question ends with a vowel, it answers "no." What the victim does is make up his own story which is supposed to be a naked revealing of his Unconscious.

This game is recommended only for your worst enemies— or people you plan to put in that category.

If you're really looking for a complicated game, or you're bored with the old pantomime quiz routine, otherwise known as THE GAME, there's a neat variation available, but you've got to be pretty hep to carry it off.

The two teams are given French phrases to work out in pantomime, rather than English. But now the complications are just beginning to start. Once the teammates have figured out what the French phrase is, they've then got to translate it into Fractured French.

For instance, if the phrase at hand is *de trop*, the team not only has to get that, but to translate it into its fractured version: Forward pass.

Or, let's say the phrase is: *crème de menthe*. To guess this alone is not enough. The team must go on to translate it to: Mystery Book of the Month Club.

Or, suppose the phrase is: *au gratin*. After this is acted out and guessed, the team must go on to get its fractured meaning—I've got a boy in prep school.

Next to Russian Roulette, this is about the most sophisticated game I can think of, and therefore marks a good point to bring all this utter nonsense to a blissful end.

But to bring a book to a close is always a rather sad experience. It's a little like the two salesmen who met in the lobby at intermission time during a performance of Arthur Miller's *Death of a Salesman*. One of them said to the other: "I hope to see you again under happier circumstances."

And then again, it's always a little awkward and difficult. Eugene Stafford sent me a clipping from the Atlanta *Constitution* which sums up the whole thing better than I could put it. A clergyman in Dawsonville, Georgia, lost an election because someone forgot to print his name on the ballot.

In this saddest of all circumstances, he told a reporter: "I have no comment—and I wouldn't know what to say if I did."

FUNK & WAGNALLS PAPERBOOKS

FUNK & WAGNALLS PAPERBOOKS